THE ESSENTIAL

11+

VERBAL REASONING

STUDY & PRACTICE BOOK

For GL Assessment

AGES 10-11

FOXTON BOOKS

With Answers

The Essential 11+ Verbal Reasoning
Study and Practice Book

First published 2021
by Foxton Books
London, UK

Copyright © Foxton Books, 2021

ISBN: 978-1-83925-077-4

Author: Jan Webley
Interior designer: Maryke Goldie
Cover designer: Ed White

Acknowledgements
Graphics: Freepik.com

FOXTON BOOKS

www.foxtonbooks.co.uk

This book provides a comprehensive guide to GL Verbal Reasoning question types. These are common types of 11+ tasks, which are used by many local authorities and schools to test suitability for selective education. The tasks and guidance in this book are suitable for Year 5 – 6 children preparing for 11+ exams, or Year 4 children working above expected progress for their age.

- **Question Types**
  Each question type is explained, with tips and examples. For each type, there is a skills section which helps develop understanding of how to approach these questions, followed by *Multiple choice* and *Open answer* questions. Finally, there is a challenge, or *Extension* section which offers tougher questions. Overall, the book contains over 460 skills practice questions.

- **Focus on Families**
  GL questions are split into types, but there are many links between these. Understanding how questions test the same skills will help children tackle multiple questions by enabling them to transfer understanding of one task to another. The *Focus on Families* section explains these links clearly and suggests games and activities to reinforce understanding.

- **Practice Papers**
  There are four timed Practice Papers which test all the GL question types, with 140 questions in total.

- **Answers section**
  Answers are provided, with explanations where appropriate, for all Question Type and Practice Paper questions.

CONTENTS

VERBAL REASONING QUESTION TYPES

1 Insert a Letter

There are TWO types of questions for *Insert a Letter*:

▶ **Multiple choice:** You will be asked to select the letter which needs to be 'inserted' in both sets of blocks to create four words. The same letter must be used in both blocks. It will end two words and start two others.

▶ **Open answer:** You will be asked to identify the letter which needs to be 'inserted' in both sets of blocks to create four words. You will not be given a choice of letters.

Top Tips

● Whichever task you are given, you need to first find a letter that can work for the first bracket.
● Then, see if it fits the second bracket. If it does, you have found the letter to insert.
● If not, look again for another letter you can use in the first blocks and repeat.
  Go through the alphabet to find possible endings and beginnings.

Skills Practice Letters with end and start words

● The most common endings for words in the English language are:
  e, t, d, s.
● The most common beginnings for words in the English language are:
  t, o, a, w, b.

To help you discover how many possible endings or beginnings words have, try finding as many letters which can start and end words as you can.

START   **FINISH**

Example: -ind

Letters which can be inserted at the beginning: b, f, k, m, r, w.
For example, bind, find, kind, etc.

Compete with a friend or family member, or a timer, to increase the challenge!

Which letters can be inserted at the **beginning of** these to make words?	Which letters can be inserted at the **end** of these to make words?
.... -and	pai- ....
.... -ore	ban- ....
.... -end	wor- ....

TYPE 1 Multiple choice

Example: Which letter can be inserted in both sets of blocks to create four words?

| nea **?** ime | bai **?** ear | **A)** r   **B)** t   **C)** n   **D)** l |

Answer: B) 't'. If we put 't' in the first set of blocks, we get 'neat' and 'time'.
If we put 't' in the second set of blocks, we get 'bait' and 'tear'.

1. Which letter can complete all four words in both sets of blocks?

| bot   ail | myt   urt | **A)** t   **B)** s   **C)** h   **D)** e |

2. Which letter can complete all four words in both sets of blocks?

| swea   able | debu   rail | **A)** r   **B)** m   **C)** l   **D)** t |

3. Which letter can complete all four words in both sets of blocks?

| sho   est | bre   ell | **A)** e   **B)** w   **C)** y   **D)** r |

4. Which letter can complete all four words in both sets of blocks?

| stor   atch | pris   edal | **A)** y   **B)** e   **C)** m   **D)** p |

5. Which letter can complete all four words in both sets of blocks?

| und   ver | als   val | **A)** e   **B)** o   **C)** s   **D)** i |

TYPE 2 Open answer

Example: Identify the letter which can complete all four words.

car **?** arn   loa **?** ome

Answer: 'd'. This would make: card, darn, load and dome.

Identify the letter which can fit into both sets of blocks to complete all four words.

1. crue   earn   fata   ever
2. alon   rode   plan   aten
3. sto   art   flo   rey
4. chai   arer   live   aked
5. wee   ome   plo   oor
6. dar   ite   lea   not
7. loo   ind   fir   ore
8. gras   ore   live   care
9. curfe   indow   sorro   asted
10. sel   are   hal   ace

EXTENSION Challenge task – Double trouble

There are two letters which can be inserted into each set of blocks. Identify the two letters and list the four words you can make with these.

1. scar   ast   Letters: _____   Words: _____
2. ban   rew   Letters: _____   Words: _____
3. cla   eak   Letters: _____   Words: _____

2 Related Words / Odd Ones Out

There are TWO types of questions for *Related Words* (also known as *Odd Ones Out*):

▶ **Multiple choice:** You will be asked to select the two words which do not belong in the group of five words. The other three will all be related to each other sharing a clear link.

▶ **Open answer:** You will be asked to identify the two words which are not related to the other three and write them out or underline them.

Top Tips

- It is important to find the three which are closely related to identify the two odd ones out. These three could be:
  — Synonyms (words with a similar meaning), e.g. dusk, sunset, evening.
  — Types of the same thing, e.g. reptiles – snake, lizard, crocodile.
  — Parts of the same thing, e.g. car parts – engine, accelerator, battery.
- Doing the same task, e.g. oven, hob, microwave.
- Sharing the same shape or quality, e.g. sphere, globe, orb.

Any relationship is possible, but the other two words will not be part of this group.

Skills Practice Making and finding families

To help you understand how these 'families' of words work, practise identifying families for these groups of words and then create your own families of words which are related.

How are these words related? Write your answer next to them.

1. pig, cow, sheep

2. frost, ice, snow

3. eyes, nose, ears

4. messy, disordered, chaotic

5. coat, jacket, anorak

Now try to create some families of related words yourself. Aim for five words or more for each family.

- Female animals
- Synonyms for 'talk'
- Shades of blue
- Farm machinery
- Human body organs (inside)
- Sports played with a bat

TYPE 1 Multiple choice

Example: Which two words are not related to the others? Select both words.

A) calf   **B)** sow   **C)** cub   **D)** foal   **E)** mare

Answer: B (sow) and E (mare). These are female animals and the other three are baby animals.

1. Which two words are not related to the others? Select both words by ringing the letters.

   A) door   **B)** close   **C)** window   **D)** shut   **E)** seal

2. Which two words are not related to the others? Select both words by ringing the letters.

   A) euro   **B)** century   **C)** cent   **D)** exchange   **E)** sterling

3. Which two words are not related to the others? Select both words by ringing the letters.

   A) tree   **B)** trunk   **C)** branch   **D)** twig   **E)** leaf

4. Which two words are not related to the others? Select both words by ringing the letters.

   A) persuade   **B)** cajole   **C)** believe   **D)** coax   **E)** guess

5. Which two words are not related to the others? Select both words by ringing the letters.

   A) letter   **B)** send   **C)** post   **D)** envelope   **E)** dispatch

TYPE 2 Open answer

Example: Which two words are the odd ones out?

guitar, music, piano, drums, volume

Answer: 'music' and 'volume'. The others are all musical instruments.

Which two words are the odd ones out?

1. colour, face, tint, draw, hue

2. pigsty, horse, trough, kennel, stable

3. nephew, sister, father, daughter, mother

4. bicycle, road, lorry, rail, bus

5. hide, seek, conceal, cover, top

6. dog, herd, pack, wolf, flock

7. create, artist, design, invent, painting

8. ghost, grave, spirit, spectre, afterlife

9. mahogany, board, oak, tree, pine

10. author, drama, novelist, playwright, biography

EXTENSION Challenge task – Family reunion

There are four families of words here. Colour code or list them to sort them into groups.

miniscule	tulip	microscopic	liver
lung	heart	cherry	compact
carnation	scarlet	rose	tiny
spleen	minute	bladder	vermilion
ruby	orchid	miniature	lily

QUESTION TYPE

3 Word-Letter Codes

There are TWO types of questions for *Word-Letter Codes*:

▶ **Encoding:** You will be given an example of a word and an example of how it has been 'encoded'. This is like a secret language such as spies use or like one you may make up with friends. You will need to work out how the encoding is working and turn another word into code.

▶ **Decoding:** You will be given coded words and asked to work out the original word. You will be given an example and need to use the same code as that.

Top Tips

- You need an alphabet for this as it is simply a case of moving forwards or backwards along the alphabet.

- Encoding and decoding treat the alphabet like numbers. The code adds or takes away letters as if they were numbers.

- Sometimes the code is the same all the way through, adding or taking away the same number of letters. Sometimes it changes.

  A B C D E F G H I J K L M N O P Q R S T U V W X Y Z

Encoding

Take your first name to practise with, e.g. *JAN*

- If I added one letter (+1) each time, JAN would become KBO.

J	A	N
+1	+1	+1
K	B	O

- If I added two letters (+2) each time, JAN would be **encoded** as LCP.
- If I subtracted one letter (–1) each time, JAN would be **encoded** as IZM.
  NB: A goes back to Z and Z goes forward to A.

Decoding

- When you decode, you reverse the code to see what the original word was, so if it was +1, it becomes –1.

K	B	O
–1	–1	–1
J	A	N

- The code KBO stands for JAN.
- These are often easier as the answer is always a real word rather than a list of letters, so you know when you are right.

A code could alternate (every other letter), so you would add one letter (+1) and then add two letters (+2) and then add one letter again, etc. JAN would be **encoded** as KCO.

Skills Practice My secret language

A B C D E F G H I J K L M N O P Q R S T U V W X Y Z

Change your first name into code. Try these.

1. +1   Name: _____   Code: _____
2. +2   Name: _____   Code: _____
3. −1   Name: _____   Code: _____
4. −2   Name: _____   Code: _____

TYPE 1 Encoding

Example: If the code for SUN is UWP, what is the code for STAR?

Answer: STAR is UVCT.

The code is +2 each time. S becomes U; T becomes V; A becomes C; R becomes T.

A B C D E F G H I J K L M N O P Q R S T U V W X Y Z

1. If the code for FISH is ILVK, what is the code for CHIPS? _____
2. If the code for NOSE is LMQC, what is the code for SMELL? _____
3. If the code for TABLE is UCCNF, what is the code for SOFA? _____
4. If the code for TIGER into XMKIV, what is the code for LION? _____
5. A coding system turns APPLE into XMMIB. What is FIG? _____
6. A coding system turns SNOW into VQRZ. What is FROST? _____
7. A coding system turns CLOUD into AJMSB. What is RAIN? _____
8. A coding system turns PENCIL into RGPEKN. What is RULER? _____

TYPE 2 Decoding

Example: If PJKIX is the code for LIGHT, what does HBVL mean?

Answer: HBVL means DARK.

The code is −4, −1, −4, −1 (alternating). H −4 is **D**; B −1 is **A**; V −4 is **R**; L − 1 is **K**.

A B C D E F G H I J K L M N O P Q R S T U V W X Y Z

1. If BHQBKD is the code for CIRCLE, what does RPTZQD mean? _____
2. If MFUUD is the code for HAPPY, what does XFI mean? _____
3. If LVOQ is the code for JUMP, what does QWGS mean? _____
4. If JROG is the code for GOLD, what does SHDUO mean? _____
5. If NGRA is the code for MEOW, what does CCUO mean?

EXTENSION Challenge task – Mission accomplished

Mission: You have cracked the **Spy Code** (+1). Now, can you work out what the enemy are planning to do by decoding this message you have intercepted:

XF XJMM BUUBDL UIF CSJEHF GSPN UIF XFTU BU NJEOJHIU PO KBOVBSZ UFOUI.

> Remember you have to −1 to decode though.

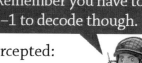

QUESTION TYPE 4 | Closest Meaning

There are TWO types of questions for *Closest Meaning*:

▶ **Multiple choice:** You have to choose the two words 'closest' in meaning out of five words. Multiple choice questions will give you pairs of words to select from. This does narrow the options, so could be helpful. You might also be asked to pick an option which is closest in meaning to a word given in the question.

▶ **Open answer:** You need to choose the two words 'closest' in meaning by writing or picking out the two words.

Top Tips

- Out of five words, two will be 'closest' in meaning.
- There may be more words which have similar meanings (synonyms), so look closely.
- Often, there will be a word with an opposite meaning, so eliminate this first, along with those which are definitely not similar in meaning.
- Then, choose the two words which are 'closer' than any other pairs.
- If there are a few options, use the strength or degree of it to help you. For example 'enormous' and 'huge' are closer than 'large' as they suggest a bigger scale.
- Most of the questions have five adjectives or verbs in them as it is easier to find describing or doing words with close alternatives, like 'cold' and 'freezing' or 'jump' and 'leap'. Sometimes, you will get nouns such as 'baby' and 'infant'.
- Your two words should share the same word class, e.g. adjective.
- If you do not know the word, look at the prefix or the root word to help you with the meaning.

Skills Practice Keeping it close

How many words can you find which are 'close' in meaning to this verb, adjective and noun?

Hello Talk (verb)	
Angry (adjective)	
Box (noun)	

TYPE 1 Multiple choice

Example: Which word is closest in meaning to 'transparent'?
   dark   translucent   cloudy   mirror   trace

Answer: The answer is 'translucent'. The prefix provides a useful clue. 'Opaque' is an antonym.

1.   Which word is closest in meaning to 'bright'?
   A) sun   **B)** luminous   **C)** colour   **D)** lights   **E)** fire

2. Which word is closest in meaning to 'calm'?
A) quiet   **B)** loud   **C)** unruffled   **D)** sleep   **E)** cold

3. Which word is closest in meaning to 'break'?
A) temporary   **B)** throw   **C)** snack   **D)** fracture   **E)** stare

4. Which word is closest in meaning to 'request'?
A) require   **B)** demand   **C)** buy   **D)** answer   **E)** adventure

5. Which word is closest in meaning to 'phase'?
A) period   **B)** word   **C)** lost   **D)** sad   **E)** post

6. Which two words are closest in meaning?
deliver   ascend   cross   climb   emerge

A) deliver and ascend   **B)** cross and climb
C) deliver and emerge   **D)** climb and ascend

7. Which two words are closest in meaning?
ordinary   fake   authentic   exceptional   original

A) ordinary and fake   **B)** original and authentic
C) exceptional and authentic   **D)** fake and original

8. Which two words are closest in meaning?
absurd   cross   wrong   bizarre   conventional

A) absurd and cross   **B)** wrong and bizarre
C) bizarre and absurd   **D)** conventional and wrong

TYPE 2 Open answer

Example: Which two words are closest in meaning?
         fluff, fur, skin, hair, feather
Answer: The answer is 'fur' and 'hair'.
         One covers the skin of animals and the other the skin of humans.

1. Which two words are closest in meaning?
bowl   plate   tray   basin   vase

2. Which two words are closest in meaning?
attack   growl   purr   rumble   snarl

3. Which two words are closest in meaning?
stir   share   strain   sieve   flush

4. Which two words are closest in meaning?
infuriated   argument   terrible   joyous   enraged

5. Which two words are closest in meaning?
behaviour   skill   honour   ability   success

6. Which two words are closest in meaning?
sad   funeral   grief   sorrow   celebrate

EXTENSION Challenge task – Pairing up

Pair up these challenging words with the word closest in meaning. Look them up if you are not sure.

relent	permissive
cutlass	boundless
lenient	yield
infinite	powerful
potent	rapier

5 Hidden Words

There are TWO types of questions for *Hidden Words*:

▶ **Multiple choice:** You will be asked to select two words which contain the hidden word. The hidden word will be made from the end of one word and the start of the word next to it.

▶ **Open answer:** You will be asked to find the four-letter hidden word in a sentence and write out the word in a space provided.

Top Tips

- Whichever task you are given, you need to start at the beginning of the sentence and look between each pair of words.
- You must find a four-letter word. Start between the first two words and then work your way across the sentence or through the options.
- It helps to write out the letters or use a highlighter to check it is a word.

Skills Practice Words within words

To help you get used to finding hidden words, try playing this game. You will need a really long word. Try finding new ones you do not know in a dictionary.

Then, find as many four-letter words within the word as you can. Look for the consecutive ones first (in the order the letters appear in the word).
Compete with a friend or family member with a timer to increase the challenge!

Example: confidentially

Answer: **Four-letter words:** dent, find, land, lent, cold, clad, fond, late, clot, dean, laid, deal, dole, load, call, fall, tall, lean, note, coat, etc.
Can you find any more?

Try seeing how many four-letter words you can find in these words or choose your own words.

- **committee** ....

- **pronunciation** ....

- **government** ....

- **collaboratively** ....

- **hospitality** ....

TYPE 1 Multiple choice

Example: Which two words contain the hidden four-letter word in this sentence?
The doctor operated on four patients that day.

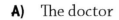 

    A) The doctor   **B)** doctor operated **C)** operated on   **D)** patients that

Answer: The hidden word is 'rope'. It appears between 'doctor' and 'operated' so the answer is B).

1. Which words contain the hidden four-letter word?
You don't wear a hat and scarf indoors.

    A) You don't   **B)** wear a hat   **C)** hat and   **D)** scarf indoors

2. Which words contain the hidden four-letter word?
It was very early to be waking up.

    A) was very   **B)** very early   **C)** be waking   **D)** waking up

3. Which words contain the hidden four-letter word?
The class chose a film for their treat.

    A) The class   **B)** class have   **C)** for their   **D)** their treat

4. Which words contain the hidden four-letter word?
The teacher told the boy not to push other children.

    A) The teacher   **B)** teacher told   **C)** push other   **D)** other children

TYPE 2 Open answer

Example: Find the four-letter word hidden in this sentence.
Elliot's father eats lots of pancakes for breakfast.

Answer: 'slot'. This four-letter word is found between 'eats' and 'lots'.

Find the four-letter words hidden in these sentences.

1. She could not wait to hug one of the puppies.

2. He ached everywhere after the run.

3. In the distance, there was a gigantic, old building.

4. Right now, Fred would love nothing better than cake.

5. Each attempt was worse than her last.

6. Everyone assumed they were staying home for Christmas.

7. Her gran had always collected items of furniture.

8. Edith's rude episode shocked everyone in class.

9. Local, ordinary people were angry about the development.

10. Though doomed, the soldier continued the lone attack.

11. Emma stood her ground between the goal posts.

12. The bike required complex amendments to its design.

EXTENSION Challenge task – Tough words

Can you find the challenging four-letter words in these sentences?

1. The children all have too many toys.

2. In this pressurised situation, she had to keep anger under control.

If you did not know these words, look them up in a dictionary afterwards.

13

6 Missing Word

There are TWO types of questions for *Missing Word*:

▶ **Multiple choice:** You will be given four or five 3-letter words which could be the missing word. You need to work out the correct one. This is easier than open answer questions, but it is vital that you can spell the complete word in capitals, otherwise you could get it wrong.

▶ **Open answer:** You will have to work out what the missing word is without any options. This means you will need to write out the complete word in capitals to see which letters are missing.

Top Tips

- A 3-letter word will complete a partial word written in capitals.
- The word will be in a sentence which will give you clues about what the word should be.
- Read the sentence carefully to help you find the clues.
- Once you know what the word in capitals is, write it out, spelling it correctly.
- Highlight or underline the three letters you have added to complete it.
- These will make a 3-letter word. If they do not, check the spelling.
- If you are given options to choose from, some will be similar, so check you know the spelling of the word, e.g. tin, tan, ten.
- You must choose the 3-letter word which spells the word in capitals correctly.

Skills Practice Spot the word

Practise finding 3-letter words within words. Each of these words has a 3-letter word hidden in it. The word will be written consecutively, meaning the order of the letters stays the same, e.g. especi**all**y – **all** is the 3-letter word. Some have more than one 3-letter word.

Find the 3-letter words written consecutively in these words.

1. student ....

2. careless ....

3. opening ....

4. expand ....

5. attend ....

6. desperate ....

TYPE 1 Multiple choice

Example: Which 3-letter word will complete the word in capitals?
The doctor still had one more PANT to see before lunch.

A) TEN   **B)** TIE   **C)** TAN   **D)** END

Answer: The answer is 'TIE'. A doctor will be seeing a PATIENT.
The letters of TIE complete the word.

14

1. Which 3-letter word will complete the word in capitals?
   The STARD of competition was extremely high that year.

   A) RED   **B)** AND   **C)** LET   **D)** EAR   **E)** JAR

2. Which 3-letter word will complete the word in capitals?
   The fabric was not suitable as it was TRANRENT.

   A) ARE   **B)** SET   **C)** SPA   **D)** EEL   **E)** PEA

3. Which 3-letter word will complete the word in capitals?
   After it started to pour with rain, the dog WPERED to go home.

   A) LET   **B)** HIS   **C)** ART   **D)** HIM   **E)** HER

4. Which 3-letter word will complete the word in capitals?
   After two hours, Ella's essay was nearly COMPE.

   A) LIT   **B)** PAL   **C)** TEN   **D)** TIN   **E)** LET

5. Which 3-letter word will complete the word in capitals?
   All the children gasped when they saw the HIPPOAMUS open its mouth.

   A) ATE   **B)** PET   **C)** POT   **D)** PIE   **E)** POP

6. Which 3-letter word will complete the word in capitals?
   As the sun rose, the TEMPEURE went higher and higher.

   A) RAT   **B)** RYE   **C)** RAN   **D)** PET   **E)** MEN

TYPE 2 Open answer

Example: Which missing 3-letter word is needed to complete the word in capitals?
         The BUILG next to her house was vacant.

Answer: DIN. The 3-letter word completes the word 'BUILDING'.

Which 3-letter words will complete the words in capitals?

1. They celebrated their mother's birthday at a local RESTAUT.   ....

2. Conor FRED when he saw how much wood he had to chop.   ....

3. The INHAANTS of the town objected to the new road.   ....

4. A local woman had been bitten by a POIOUS snake.   ....

5. The reading COMPRESION was from Harry Potter.   ....

6. Oliver found some of the other children's attitude IMURE.   ....

7. Without MAINANCE, the shed would collapse.   ....

8. Elsie was excellent at division and MULTIPLIION.   ....

9. Pollution is bad for the ENVIRONT.   ....

10. In the orchard, there was so much fruit that it was ADANT.   ....

EXTENSION Challenge task – Matching the T words

Complete the words by matching them with their missing 3-letter words.

DISHEARED	TIN
CONUE	TON
MONOY	TAN
RECGLE	TEN

7 Letters for Numbers

There are TWO types of questions for *Letters for Numbers*:

▶ **Multiple choice:** You will be given up to five letters, each of which equals a different number. You will be given a sum in letters, like A + B – C, and will need to work out the answer as a letter. Your choice of answers will include the letter.

▶ **Open answer:** These work exactly like multiple choice questions, but you will just need to record the letter. You may be required to record the answer as a number as well, so read instructions carefully.

Top Tips

- You will be told what each letter is as a number.
- There will be a sum written in letters.
- Turn the letter sum into a sum with numbers, so it looks like a normal mathematics task.
- Work out the answer to the sum as a number.
- Turn the number back into a letter for the answer.
- The answer to each question will be one of the letters, so that should be simple. If not, you know it is not right.
- Do the sum in the order it appears (not BODMAS).

Skills Practice   The first stage

This is like any other code. Change the letters to numbers and work out the sum.
To start with, just write the answer as a *number*.

$$A = 5 \quad B = 2 \quad C = 4 \quad D = 6 \quad E = 3$$

1. $C \times D = $ _____   **2.** $B + E = $ _____

3. $A \times E = $ _____   **4.** $A + B + C = $ _____

5. $D + C - B = $ _____

TYPE 1   Multiple choice

Example: Write the answer to this sum as a letter.

$$A = 8 \quad B = 3 \quad C = 10 \quad D = 5 \quad E = 2$$
$$C - A + B = ?$$

Answer: The sum is: $10 - 8 + 3 = 5 = $ **D**.

1. What is the answer to this sum as a letter? Ring the letter.

$$A = 4 \quad B = 9 \quad C = 6 \quad D = 8 \quad E = 2$$
$$A + C - E = ? \qquad \qquad \qquad \qquad \qquad \quad \text{A} \quad \text{B} \quad \text{C} \quad \text{D} \quad \text{E}$$

2. What is the answer to this sum as a letter? Ring the letter.

$$A = 14 \quad B = 7 \quad C = 4 \quad D = 2 \quad E = 10$$
$$B \times D - C = ? \qquad \qquad \qquad \qquad \qquad \quad \text{A} \quad \text{B} \quad \text{C} \quad \text{D} \quad \text{E}$$

3. What is the answer to this sum as a letter? Ring the letter.
A = 5   B = 50   C = 100   D = 20   E = 10

D × A – B = ?   ....   A   B   C   D   E

4. What is the answer to this sum as a letter? Ring the letter.
A = 4   B = 16   C = 14   D = 2   E = 12

E + D + A – D = ?   ....   A   B   C   D   E

5. What is the answer to this sum as a letter? Ring the letter.
A = 19   B = 17   C = 15   D = 13   E = 11

C + B – A = ?   ....   A   B   C   D   E

TYPE 2 Open answer

These work in the same way, but you have to write out the letter, rather than ring it. You might also be asked to write the answer as a number.

Write the answer to these sums in *letters*.

1.

J	K	L	M	N
4	9	5	7	6

K – N + J = ?   ....

2.

W	U	Z	X	Y
8	2	12	4	6

Z ÷ X × U = ?   ....

3.

R	S	T	U	V
20	36	8	32	7

V × T – R = ?   ....

4.

E	F	G	H	I
3	16	14	9	21

I ÷ E + H = ?   ....

5.

L	M	N	O	P
15	1	4	6	17

P – M ÷ N = ?   ....

Write the answer to these sums in *numbers*. Do the sums in order (not BODMAS).

6.

P	Q	R	S	T
12	6	3	8	10

P × Q + T = ?   ....

7.

D	E	F	G	H
7	9	5	4	2

F + D + G = ?   ....

8.

G	L	X	R	P
8	13	9	15	22

X × G – P = ?   ....

9.

A	B	C	D	E
2	4	8	16	32

E – D + B ÷ A = ?   ....

10.

R	L	V	M	J
10	1	11	100	101

J + M – L + R = ?   ....

EXTENSION Challenge task – Mighty maths

Do this sum and write the answer as a *letter*. Do it in order (not BODMAS).
A = 8   B = 12   C = 4   D = 10   E = 2

B × A ÷ E ÷ C – A = ?   ....

17

QUESTION TYPE 8 Move a Letter

There are TWO types of questions for *Move a Letter*:

◗ **Multiple choice:** You will be given two words and need to identify which letter from the first word can be moved to the second word to create two new words. The options will be letters from the first word.

◗ **Open answer:** These will ask you to write out the two new words created by moving a letter from the first to the second word. This means you need to work out the right letter and then write out the two new words which will be made.

Top Tips

- First look carefully at the first word (word on the left).
- Identify any letter you can remove while still leaving a word, as in 'crave' – we can move the 'r' and leave 'cave'.
- If only one letter can be removed and still leave a word, this must be the one you add to the second word (word on the right), as in 'r' can be added to 'cat' to make 'cart'.
- If more than one letter can be taken from the first word, then you need to try both letters with the second word, to see which one works.
  If your first word is 'crash', you could take the 'c' away and have 'rash' or the 'r' away and have 'cash'. However, only one of these letters will be able to be added to the second word.
- You cannot alter the order of any letters to make it work.
- If you get stuck, try writing the first word out with a different letter missing each time.

Skills Practice The first extraction

Like a dentist extracting a tooth, you need to extract the right letter from the first word.

Identify the letter/s you can remove from each of these words, to leave a new word.

1. brand   Letter _____ (2 letters)
2. toast   Letter _____
3. flew   Letter _____
4. cloud   Letter _____ (2 letters)
5. trout   Letters _____ (3 letters)

Some have 2 or 3 'teeth' you can extract!

TYPE 1 Multiple choice

Example: Which letter can be moved from the first word to the second word to create two new words? Do not alter the order.

black   hat

A) b   **B)** l   **C)** c   **D)** k

Answer: 1. You could extract 'b' or 'l', leaving 'lack' and 'back'. Only 'l' can be added to 'hat', making 'halt'.

Which letter do you need to move from the first to the second word, to create two new words? Do not alter the order of any letters.

1.	gland	*sped*	**A)** g	**B)** l	**C)** n	**D)** d
2.	with	*bat*	**A)** w	**B)** i	**C)** t	**D)** h
3.	brush	*heat*	**A)** b	**B)** r	**C)** s	**D)** h
4.	lime	*chap*	**A)** l	**B)** i	**C)** m	**D)** e
5.	slang	*ream*	**A)** l	**B)** s	**C)** n	**D)** g
6.	grown	*ham*	**A)** g	**B)** r	**C)** w	**D)** n
7.	rifle	*let*	**A)** e	**B)** r	**C)** l	**D)** f
8.	taupe	*bond*	**A)** u	**B)** t	**C)** a	**D)** e
9.	coast	*curse*	**A)** c	**B)** o	**C)** a	**D)** s
10.	paint	*runs*	**A)** p	**B)** a	**C)** i	**D)** t

TYPE 2 Open answer

Example: Which two new words can you make by moving one letter from the first word and adding it to second? You cannot change the order of the letters.

orange   slid

Answer: range and solid. Move the 'o' from 'orange' and add it to 'slid'.

Which two new words can you make by moving one letter from the first word and adding it to second? You cannot change the order of the letters.

1.	brand	*spot*	.... and ....
2.	tilled	*sat*	.... and ....
3.	fiend	*gene*	.... and ....
4.	toaster	*shut*	.... and ....
5.	train	*sick*	.... and ....
6.	feast	*wait*	.... and ....
7.	could	*pond*	.... and ....
8.	chore	*torn*	.... and ....
9.	poise	*clam*	.... and ....
10.	clever	*pat*	.... and ....

EXTENSION Challenge task – Painful extraction

These are some tricky ones as the words created might be less familiar to you. You may need a dictionary to check if they are words!

WORDS

1.	huge	*bade*	.... and ....
2.	troupe	*prod*	.... and ....
3.	drown	*heath*	.... and ....
4.	naive	*wave*	.... and ....
5.	beast	*ally*	.... and ....

9 Letter Series

There are TWO types of questions for *Letter Series*:

▶ **Multiple choice:** You need to find the next pair of letters in the series. As with other alphabet questions, this is done by treating letters like numbers. For multiple choice questions, you will be given options of different pairs of letters.

▶ **Open answer:** These will ask you to write out the next two letters (pair) in the series, with no options to choose from.

Top Tips

- Always have the alphabet in front of you to help.
- These are letter series, but it will help to think of them as number series to start.
- Think about how you move from one to the other, working out how many you add or take away each time.
- The pattern could be the same, like adding 1 or 2 each time, or it could change by increasing or decreasing in number, or even alternating between two numbers.

Treat each letter in the pair as a separate sequence and do it in two steps:

- First letters of the pairs – how do they move in the sequence?
- Second letters of the pairs – how do they move in the sequence?

If you get to the end of the alphabet (Z), start again at A. Similarly, if you are subtracting and get to A, go to Z.

Skills Practice One at a time

A B C D E F G H I J K L M N O P Q R S T U V W X Y Z

Although these letter series have pairs of letters, it is easier to start with just one letter sequences. Look at how this series works.

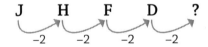

This means the next letter in this series is B, as it is D – 2.
Try these ones. Write them out and use the alphabet and your own arrows to help you.

1. B   C   E   H   ?

2. N   Q   T   W   ?

3. M   L   K   J   ?

4. F   G   I   J   ?

TYPE 1 Multiple choice

A B C D E F G H I J K L M N O P Q R S T U V W X Y Z

Example: Which pair of letters should be next in this sequence?

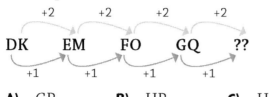

DK   EM   FO   GQ   ??

A) GR   **B)** HR   **C)** HS   **D)** KL

Answer: HS. The first letters form a series where you add one (+1), making DEFG and then **H**. The second letters form a series where you add two (+2), making KMOQ and then **S**.

Which pair of letters should be next in these series?

1.	PG	QF	RE	SD	?	**A)** UD	**B)** TC	**C)** TE	**D)** RB
2.	DD	FE	HF	JG	?	**A)** CC	**B)** EH	**C)** MI	**D)** LH
3.	MK	NL	PM	SN	?	**A)** VO	**B)** WO	**C)** WP	**D)** KM
4.	WR	UP	SN	QL	?	**A)** RJ	**B)** OJ	**C)** TM	**D)** OK
5.	VJ	WK	YL	BM	?	**A)** FN	**B)** ZN	**C)** EO	**D)** RL

TYPE 2 Open answer

A B C D E F G H I J K L M N O P Q R S T U V W X Y Z

Example: Complete the letter series by adding the next pair of letters.

EJ   IL   MN   QP   ?

Answer: UR. The first letters form a series where you add four (+4), making EIMQ and then **U**. The second letters form a series where you add two (+2), making JLNP and then **R**.

Complete these letter series by adding the next pair of letters.

1.	NW	PU	RS	TQ	_____	**2.**	KD	LC	NB	QA	_____
3.	HS	KP	NM	QJ	_____	**4.**	WF	XH	YJ	ZL	_____
5.	YD	TE	PF	MG	_____	**6.**	IP	KR	MT	OV	_____
7.	AF	CG	BH	DI	_____	**8.**	JJ	MI	PH	SG	_____

EXTENSION Challenge task – Mirror, mirror

Sometimes, the series are made up of letters which mirror each other in the alphabet. Think of M and N in the middle mirroring each other, or A and Z, then B and Y.

A B C D E F G H I J K L M N O P Q R S T U V W X Y Z
Z Y X W V U T S R Q P O N M L K J I H G F E D C B A

Work out the mirror of these letters by counting inwards or outwards along the alphabet:

1. G _____   **2.** D _____   **3.** Q _____

Look for a mirror if letters do not have an obvious pattern.

10 Word Connections

There are TWO types of questions for *Word Connections*:

▶ **Multiple choice:** You choose the pair of words which completes the sentence so it makes sense. This will reveal similar connections or relationships.

▶ **Open answer:** You write out or underline the two words which complete the sentence, one from each set of blocks. This will reveal similar connections or relationships.

Top Tips

- Word connections are about relationships.
- You need to choose two words from blocks which complete the sentence you are given.
- To start, identify the relationship and express it in words, for example, 'is part of' or 'can be found' or 'does this function'.
- Then check if you can make the same statement about both word relationships.

These are some possible relationships the words might create:

- Synonyms or antonyms of words
- Places – the people or things are found in this place, or an action is done here
- Type or example of – such as type of shellfish or chemical
- Function – such as lungs and gills used for breathing, or function of a tradesperson
- Gender and age – such as female or young animals
- Grammar – such as the same tense of a verb

Skills Practice Getting connected

There are five connections shown in this chart.
Pair the words and describe how they are connected.

piglet	plus	lizard	fridge	football
snake	cold	play	add	foal

1. _____ and _____ Connection: _____
2. _____ and _____ Connection: _____
3. _____ and _____ Connection: _____
4. _____ and _____ Connection: _____
5. _____ and _____ Connection: _____

TYPE 1 Multiple choice

Example: Which two words from the blocks do you need to complete the sentence?
Your choices must show the same connection or relationship.
Good is to (great, product, better) as bad is to (worse, mouldy, evil).
A) product, mouldy **B)** great, mouldy   **C)** great, evil   **D)** better, worse

Answer: D, 'better, worse'. Both of these are comparatives of the original words, 'good' and 'bad'.

1. Which two words from the blocks do you need to complete the sentence?
Heart is to (beat, pump, organ) as leg is to (two, foot, limb).

   A) beat, foot   **B)** organ, limb   **C)** organ, two   **D)** pump, limb

2. Which two words from the blocks do you need to complete the sentence?
Mechanic is to (mend, garage, car) as surgeon is to (doctor, mask, theatre).

   A) mend, mask   **B)** garage, theatre   **C)** car, doctor   **D)** garage, mask

3. Which two words from the blocks do you need to complete the sentence?
String is to (ball, round, guitar) as key is to (lock, piano, door).

   A) guitar, piano   **B)** ball, lock   **C)** round, door   **D)** ball, piano

4. Which two words from the blocks do you need to complete the sentence?
Clear is to (sure, opaque, wipe) as help is to (care, give, hinder).

   A) sure, care   **B)** wipe, give   **C)** opaque, care   **D)** opaque, hinder

5. Which two words from the blocks do you need to complete the sentence?
Nine is to (10, 90, 21) as thirty is to (15, 33, 300).

   A) 10, 15   **B)** 21, 33   **C)** 90, 300   **D)** 90, 33

TYPE 2 Open answer

Example: Which two words from the blocks do you need to complete the sentence?
Your choices must show the same relationship.
Mother is to (care, home, baby) as mare is to (horse, foal, gallop).

Answer: **baby, foal.** Both show parent/child relationships:
a mother has a baby, and a mare has a foal.

Which two words from the blocks do you need to complete the sentence? Your choices must show the same relationship. **Highlight** or **underline** the two correct words.

1. **plus** is to (size, add, more) as **times** is to (clock, hour, multiply).

2. **county** is to (town, village, country) as **country** is to (side, continent, map).

3. **sow** is to (crop, pig, needle) as **cow** is to (fear, elephant, farm).

4. **sun** is to (hot, swim, summer) as **snow** is to (winter, Christmas, frost).

5. **orchestra** is to (instrument, musician, song) as **library** is to (read, book, educate).

6. **doctor** is to (heal, medicine, pain) as **builder** is to (house, brick, construction).

7. **waist** is to (stomach, measure, waste) as **would** is to (could, wood, try).

8. **iris** is to (eye, flower, colour) as **beech** is to (sea, whale, tree).

9. **lamb** is to (sheep, wool, bleat) as **tiger** is to (baby, roar, stripes).

10. **letter** is to (write, post, sign) as **email** is to (work, message, send).

11. **hand** is to (pass, leg, touch) as **ear** is to (head, hear, here).

12. **jump** is to (exercise, play, bump) as **run** is to (sun, park, summer).

EXTENSION Challenge task – It's off to work we go ...

Draw lines to connect up the professions and the materials they work with.

architect	spacecraft	files	archaeologist	archivist
accountant	buildings	astronaut	figures	ruins

23

11 Number Series

There are TWO types of questions for *Number Series*:

▶ **Multiple choice:** You identify out how the sequence works and choose the number which completes the number series correctly.

▶ **Open answer:** You identify and write the missing number in the series. You will need to know how the sequence works to calculate this.

Top Tips

- Number series or sequences are about rules which govern which number comes next.
- These work in the same way as *Letter Series* questions.
- To identify the sequence, think about how you move from one number to the next. This operation could be through any of the basic mathematics operations (+ − × ÷).
- The pattern could be the same, like adding or subtracting 1 or 2 each time.
- Sometimes the numbers ascend (+1, +2, +3, etc.) or descend, or do this alternately (+1, −1, +2, −2).
- Sometimes you have to halve, double, square or cube numbers.
- Check the first three operations as the series may alternate.

Skills Practice Basic operations

Once you work out what operation you have to do each time, you can use this to calculate the missing number. It may be at the end or somewhere else.

Look at how this series works with an addition operation.

8   11   14   17   ?

This means the next letter in this series is 20, as it is 17 + 3 = 20.

Try these ones which use the different mathematics operations. Write them out and use the alphabet and your own arrows to help you.

1.	Addition:	10	12	14	?	18
2.	Subtraction:	35	30	?	20	15
3.	Multiplication:	2	4	8	16	?
4.	Division:	243	?	27	9	3

TYPE 1 Multiple choice

Example: Which number should be in the brackets for this series?

10 100 1000

×10 ×10 ×10

A) 100 **B)** 1000 **C)** 10,000 **D)** 100,000

Answer: C. The operation is ×10 each time, or add a 0. The next number is 10,000.

Choose the correct numbers to complete these number series.

1. 4 8 12 16

A) 18 **B)** 20 **C)** 22 **D)** 24

2. 82 70 58 46

A) 40 **B)** 42 **C)** 38 **D)** 34

3. 3 10 17 31

A) 24 **B)** 21 **C)** 27 **D)** 23

4. 15 20 30 35

A) 40 **B)** 45 **C)** 50 **D)** 55

5. 18 36 144 288

A) 80 **B)** 92 **C)** 78 **D)** 72

TYPE 2 Open answer

Example: Complete the number series by identifying the missing number.

12 24 36 48

+12 +12 +12 +12

Answer: 60. The operation is +12 (or 12 times table), so 48 + 12 = 60.

Complete these number series by adding the missing numbers.

1. 5 10 20 40   **2.** 85 79 73 67

3. 18 20 24 30   **4.** 10 1 0.1   0.001

5. 95 80   50 35   **6.**   22 44 88 172

7. 786   564 453 342   **8.** 130 112 94 76

9. 49 42 35   21   **10.** 197 19.7 1.97   0.0197

EXTENSION Challenge task – All square and taking turns

Can you work out these number series?

1. 36 49 64 81   **2.** 8 27 64 125

There are 2 alternating series here. The first, third and fifth follow a pattern. The second and fourth follow a pattern.

3. 4 3 40 6   **4.** 9 8   16 27

5. 1000 12 100 17   **6.** 3 4   8 9

<table>
<tr><td>QUESTION TYPE</td></tr>
</table>

12 Compound Words

There are TWO types of questions for *Compound Words*:

▶ **Multiple choice:** You choose the pair of words which form a compound word.

▶ **Open answer:** You choose one word from each set of brackets and write out the compound word they create together.

Top Tips

- Compound words consist of two words added together, which make a new word, such as 'sunflower' or 'ladybird'.
- There will normally be two groups of words and you will need to pick one from each group.
- These two words will form a compound word.
- Write out the word you make, as it could sound right, but have the wrong spelling.
- Trying each word and pair out, in turn, can help if you are stuck.

Skills Practice The perfect partner

Some words are excellent at making compound words. For instance, we can add 'berry', 'bell', 'bird' and 'print' to **blue**, to make: *blueberry, bluebell, bluebird* and *blueprint*.

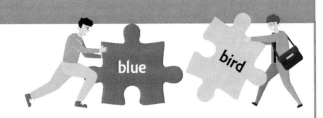

How many words can you add to each of these to make compound words?
Challenge yourself with a timer or against a friend or family member.

- some ....
- back ....
- eye ....
- in ....
- life ....

Draw lines to join up pairs of words which can make new, compound words.

jelly	is	ball	tan	station
sun	snow	fire	fish	land

TYPE 1 Multiple choice

Example: Which two words, one from each set of brackets, can make a new, compound word?

(sun, hot, sky)   **(times, glasses, plays)**

A) sun plays   **B)** hot times   **C)** sky glasses   **D)** sun glasses

Answer: The answer is D. The compound word is 'sunglasses'.

Which two words, one from each set of brackets, can make a new, compound word?

1. **(song, music, play) (hour, time, clock)**

   A) song clock   **B)** music hour   **C)** play time   **D)** song time

2. **(leg, head, arm) (skirt, shirt, dress)**

   A) leg shirt   **B)** head dress   **C)** arm skirt   **D)** head shirt

3. **(fort, castle, moat) (day, time, night)**

   A) fort night   **B)** castle time   **C)** moat day   **D)** fort time

4. **(car, house, home) (hold, hand, give)**

   A) car hold   **B)** home hand   **C)** house hold   **D)** car give

5. **(stand, sit, lie) (still, last, done)**

   A) stand last   **B)** lie done   **C)** sit still   **D)** stand still

TYPE 2 Open answer

Example: Make a compound word by taking one word from each set of brackets and combining them to make a new word.

   (car, let, coast) (on, pet, turn)

Answer: The answer is 'carpet' which is made from 'car' and 'pet'.

Make a compound word by taking one word from each set of brackets and combining them to make a new word.

1. (field, dam, land)   (corn, slide, pin)   ....
2. (ship, pass, imp)   (port, time, space)   ....
3. (swim, back, turn)   (front, pool, stroke)   ....
4. (he, on, him)   (shelf, art, fair)   ....
5. (on, over, in)   (coast, deed, able)   ....
6. (water, fountain, lake) (down, fall, drip)   ....
7. (arm, leg, foot)   (start, end, race)   ....
8. (sound, sight, smell)   (claim, trial, proof)   ....
9. (tyre, wheel, spoke)   (screen, chair, cart)   ....
10. (over, take, lend)   (seas, ships, ports)   ....

EXTENSION Challenge task – Odd ones out

1. Which of the following words cannot be combined with 'foot' to create a compound word?

   hold   fold   fall   lights   all can combine

2. Which of the following words cannot be combined with 'in' to create a compound word?

   form   side   doors   rage   all can combine

3. Which of the following words cannot be combined with 'honey' to create a compound word?

   moon   sun   suckle   comb   all can combine

4. Which of the following words cannot be combined with 'land' 'to create a compound word?

   mark   is   slide   ward   all can combine

13 Make a Word

There are TWO types of questions for *Make a Word*:

▶ **Multiple choice:** You choose the word you think can be made in the same way as the first pair.

▶ **Open answer:** You have to work out which word you could make from the second set of words, following the same order as the first pair.

Top Tips

- You need to work out how the first pair of words creates the word in brackets.
- Number the letters of the words outside of brackets from 1 to 8.
- Work out the number order of the first word in brackets, e.g. 6251.
- Number the letters of the second pair of words and then copy out the same number letters, 6251.
- This will give you the missing four-letter word to complete the brackets.
- Use 2 letters from each word.

Skills Practice Every letter counts

You need to number each letter in the two words, from 1 – 8.

c o l d   h i v e   The word **dove** is made up of letters 4, 2, 7, 8.
↓↓↓↓ ↓↓↓↓
1234 5678

1. Which numbers make up these words? Take two letters from each word.

   A) seat   bore   **beat** is made from numbers: ....

   B) race   stop   **pore** is made from numbers: ....

   C) main   plot   **tail** is made from numbers: ....

To put it simply, you have to find a word which uses two letters each from two different words.

2. See if you can do it yourself. Look at these pairs of words and find a word you can make using two letters from each. You do not need to number these.

   A) crow   lane   Word: ....

   B) fold   same   Word: ....

   C) coat   fire   Word: ....

   D) germ   boat   Word: ....

TYPE 1 Multiple choice

Example: Which word goes in the second set of brackets? It is made in the same way as the word in the first set of brackets, using letters from the two words outside the brackets.

f o u r (s o f t) s e a t   l a c k (........) b e a m
1234   5678

   A) lame   **B)** male   **C)** balm   **D)** mace

Answer: The answer is C. The letter order is 5218, making 'balm'.

Which word goes in the second set of brackets? It is made in the same way as the word in the first set of brackets using 2 letters from each of the two words outside the brackets.

1. **debt (lead) late   earn (_____) snow**

   A) wear   **B)** wane   **C)** sane   **D)** sore

2. **lone (blue) numb   reap (_____) lied**

   A) drip   **B)** leap   **C)** raid   **D)** laid

3. **kite (kind) pond   crop (_____) flew**

   A) flop   **B)** crew   **C)** role   **D)** lore

4. **malt (mean) nest   slow (_____) east**

   A) lost   **B)** west   **C)** seat   **D)** sale

5. **mule (able) back   sink (_____) atom**

   A) tins   **B)** moat   **C)** tank   **D)** most

TYPE 2 Open answer

Example: Make the word in the second brackets in the same way as the first is made.

   lock (pole) help   tank (_____) deer

Answer: rate. The answer is 'rate' which orders the letters 8216.

Which word should go in the second set of brackets, using the same order as the first?

1. boat (debt) made   vase (_____) halo
2. fume (jump) jeep   said (_____) toll
3. back (care) rent   grin (_____) once
4. lime (melt) tame   nose (_____) diva
5. hold (good) grow   neck (_____) boat
6. nail (kiln) lake   plan (_____) mule
7. raft (fork) joke   send (_____) does
8. hare (card) clod   base (_____) foot

EXTENSION Challenge task – Pair and make

FACE	MODE	VASE	KITE	ROSE
LEGS	BORE	FAIL	MAKE	PLOT

Which pairs of words can be used to create these words? List the two words from the chart above and the number order. Use 2 letters from each word. Look at the example to see how to write your answers.

Example: CANE   **Words:** RACE and DINE   **Number order:** 3278

1. ALSO   Words: _____ and _____   Number order: _____
2. GOLD   Words: _____ and _____   Number order: _____
3. CAKE   Words: _____ and _____   Number order: _____
4. BEAR   Words: _____ and _____   Number order: _____
5. STEP   Words: _____ and _____   Number order: _____

14 Letter Connections

There are TWO types of questions for *Letter Connections*:

▶ **Multiple choice:** You need to find the pair of letters which complete the sentence. The second two pairs of letters will have the same 'connection' as the first two pairs. You will be given options of different pairs of letters. As with *Letter Series* (Type 9), this is done by treating letters like numbers.

▶ **Open answer:** These will ask you to write out the two letters (pair) which complete the sentence and show the same connection as the first two pairs of letters.

Top Tips

- Always have the alphabet in front of you to help.
- These are letter series, but it will help to think of them as number series to start.
- Think about how you move from one letter to the other, working out how many you add or take away each time.
- The pattern could be the same, like adding 1 or 2 each time, or it could change by increasing or decreasing in number, or even alternating between two numbers.

Treat each letter in the pair as a separate sequence and do it in two steps:
- First letters of the pairs – how do they move in the sequence?
- Second letters of the pairs – how do they move in the sequence?

Do this same movement to the pair in the question, with two different steps so it 'connects' in the same way.

Skills Practice One at a time

A B C D E F G H I J K L M N O P Q R S T U V W X Y Z

As with *Letter Series*, start with 1 letter. **F is to K as L is to** _____

To get from F to K, we must +5. To repeat this connection, we must +5 to L.
This gives us Q, so the final sentence is:

F is to K as L is to Q.

+5   +5

Try these ones. Write them out and use the alphabet and your own arrows to help you.

1. D is to B as V is to _____

2. O is to T as G is to _____

3. S is to N as J is to _____

4. A is to Z as B is to _____

TYPE 1 Multiple choice

A B C D E F G H I J K L M N O P Q R S T U V W X Y Z

Example: Which pair of letters are needed to complete this sentence?

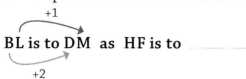

BL is to DM as HF is to _____

A) KH   **B)** IG   **C)** JG   **D)** FO

Answer: JG. The first letters form a series where you add 2 (+2), so H + 2 = **J**.
The second letters form a series where you add 1 (+1), so F + 1 = **G**.

A B C D E F G H I J K L M N O P Q R S T U V W X Y Z

Identify the pairs of letters which complete these sentences and show the same connection.

1.   KV is to MU as DJ is to _____
   A)   LT   **B)**   FI   **C)**   EK   **D)**   OX

2.   PX is to LZ as NO is to _____
   A)   RR   **B)**   KZ   **C)**   PQ   **D)**   JQ

3.   BR is to ET as SK is to _____
   A)   VM   **B)**   HV   **C)**   UN   **D)**   RJ

4.   RB is to UZ as FN is to _____
   A)   HP   **B)**   XD   **C)**   IL   **D)**   DO

5.   NR is to LU as JI is to _____
   A)   PX   **B)**   KM   **C)**   MJ   **D)**   HL

TYPE 2 Open answer

A B C D E F G H I J K L M N O P Q R S T U V W X Y Z

Example: Complete this sentence so it makes sense and shows the same letter connections.
CY is to GW as RQ is to _____

Answer: VO. The first letters form a series where you add 4 (+4), so R + 4 = **V**.
The second letters form a series where you subtract 2 (–2), so Q – 2 = **O**.

Complete these sentences so they make sense and show the same letter connections.

1.   DD is to CB as JM is to _____   **2.**   RG is to VK as PD is to _____

3.   EW is to CS as HX is to _____   **4.**   QK is to VP as XB is to _____

5.   PH is to MI as JY is to _____   **6.**   NC is to QF as RL is to _____

7.   AB is to ZY as CD is to _____   **8.**   FR is to LT as KP is to _____

EXTENSION Challenge task – Nearest two-letter words

What do you need to add or take away to make the pairs of letters into the nearest two-letter words?

Example: NP   **Word:** on   **Sum:** +1, –1

1.   HQ   Word: _____   Sum: _____

2.   RM   Word: _____   Sum: _____

3.   SN   Word: _____   Sum: _____

QUESTION TYPE 15 Reading Information

There are TWO types of questions for *Reading Information*:

▶ **Multiple choice:** You will be given some detailed information, followed by a series of statements about the information. You will be asked to identify the one which is TRUE or FALSE.

▶ **Open answer:** You will be given some detailed information and then asked a question about it. You will need to record your answer, which might be about a person, time, figure or other information.

Top Tips

- Each question will include a paragraph of detailed information.
- The information is designed to be complicated, so find a way of ordering or organising it such as a table, a list or a diagram.
- Use your chart or list or sequence to show details like times, positions, choices taken or amounts which you can then use to find the answer or check statements.
- These often take longer than other questions, so you might want to leave until last.

Skills Practice Get organised

Always have a pen and paper at the ready for 'reading information' questions to put the details in order.

Johnny, Susie, Fred, Aya and Rifat picked strawberries for Aya's uncle and were given £20 to share based on how many strawberries they had picked. Susie had £4.50 and Rifat £2 less. Aya and Fred each got £3 and Johnny got the rest.

To organise this, start with what you know:

Children	Money paid
Susie	£4.50
Aya	£3.00
Fred	£3.00
Rifat	£2.50

If Johnny got the rest, we do this sum: 4.5 + 3 + 3 + 2.5 = £13.
Then, £20 subtract £13, which means Johnny gets £7.00.

This allows us then to answer any question. Try these:

1. Who picked the most strawberries? ....

2. Which two children picked the same amount? ....

3. Who picked the least strawberries? ....

TYPE 1 Multiple choice

Example: Spike has been given lots of sweets for his birthday so he brings them to the park. Elias eats 12 of them, while Sonia eats twice as many as him, but 5 less than Lisa. Terence is allergic, so he does not eat any but takes 10 to give to his sister. Robin eats 8 which is half as many as Spike has left. Which statement is true?

A) There are 100 sweets.

B) Sonia has the most sweets.

C) Robin has the least number of sweets.

D) Spike and Elias have the same number of sweets.

Answer: C. Robin has the least number of sweets, which is 8.

Try these ones:

1. John walks to school and back every weekday. It is 2.5 miles to his school. John walks the same distance every day for 4 weeks. Which statement is true?

A) John walks 140 miles in 4 weeks.

B) John walks the same distance for 28 consecutive days.

C) John walks 100 miles in 4 weeks.

D) John likes walking to school.

2. The football match kicks off at 3 pm. Five friends plan to meet up to watch the match. Sophie arrives first at 2.35 pm. Tamzy is 20 minutes later and Florence is 10 minutes after her. Georgia arrives 25 minutes after Sophie, which is 5 minutes after Jo has arrived. Which statement is true?

A) Tamzy arrives late for the match.

B) Jo and Tamzy arrive at the same time.

C) No one is late for the match.

D) Florence arrives before Jo.

TYPE 2 Open answer

Read the information and organise it, before answering the questions.

1. Four children are in Year 5 at school.
Enrique's birthday is on 28th May.
Horace's is 7 days later.
Monica has her birthday on 5th June and Evie is the oldest of them all.

A) Whose birthday falls on the latest date in the year?

B) When is Horace's birthday?

C) Do any children share a birthday?

D) What do we know for certain about the date of Evie's birthday?

2. A train starts from the first railway station, where 26 passengers get on. At the second stop, another 18 passengers get on and 9 get off. At the third stop, 17 more passengers get on and 5 alight.

A) How many passengers are on the train between stops 1 and 2?

B) How many passengers are on the train between stops 2 and 3?

C) At the end, how many passengers are on the train?

16 Opposite Meaning

There are TWO types of questions for *Opposite Meaning*:

▶ **Multiple choice:** You will be given two brackets, each containing three words. You will have to pick the option which has the two words which are 'most' opposite in meaning. You might also be asked to choose a word most opposite to a word you are given.

▶ **Open answer:** You will be given two brackets, each containing three words. You must identify the two words which are 'most' opposite in meaning.

Top Tips

● Read the question carefully to make sure you are looking for antonyms, words with opposite meanings.

● Look out for synonyms which are put there to tempt you and be ready to eliminate these.

● Here, your vocabulary is essential: the wider it is, the easier this will be, so look up words you do not know to increase your range.

● Most antonyms will be verbs or adjectives, rather than nouns, so look for these.

● Even if you think you know the answer, take time as you need the 'most' opposite.

Skills Practice Antonym action

Antonyms are words which are 'most' opposite in meaning. Practise your ability to find these by pairing up the antonyms below.

accept	deep	profit	come
help	go	reject	hinder
simple	loss	shallow	elaborate

List the pairs of antonyms:

1. _____ and _____   **2.** _____ and _____

3. _____ and _____   **4.** _____ and _____

5. _____ and _____   **6.** _____ and _____

TYPE 1 Multiple choice

Example: Which two words are most opposite in meaning? Pick the option with these two words.

{**economical, buy, value**}   {**cheap, budget, expensive**}

A) economical/cheap   **B)** buy/budget

C) value/expensive   **D)** economical/expensive

Answer: D. **economical** means something is **cheap**, whereas **expensive** is the opposite.

Which two words are most opposite in meaning? Pick the option with these two words.

1. {humble, clever, careful}   {shy, boastful, thoughtful}

   A) clever/boastful   **B)** humble/shy   **C)** humble/boastful   **D)** clever/thoughtful

2. {tired, upset, enraged}   {energised, weary, studious}

   A) tired/weary   **B)** upset/studious   **C)** enraged/energised   **D)** tired/energised

3. {behave, punish, judge}   {reward, beat, fair}

   A) behave/beat   **B)** punish/reward   **C)** judge/fair   **D)** punish/beat

4. Pick the word which is most opposite in meaning to the word in bold. Ring or highlight it.

meagre	small	enough	large	kind
decline	accept	depreciate	oblige	desperate
idle	hero	lazy	fit	active
perish	mouldy	die	flourish	dispose
advance	attack	retreat	follow	allow
docile	wild	meek	horrible	habitat
imitation	fraud	irrigation	original	copy

TYPE 2 Open answer

Example: Choose the two words, one from each set of brackets, which are most opposite in meaning.

   {begin, betray, examine}   {commence, cease, choice}

Answer: begin and cease. The answer is 'begin' and 'cease' which mean to start and stop.

Choose the two words, one from each set of brackets, which are most opposite in meaning.

1. {think, occupy, protest}   {vacate, apart, revolution} _____ and _____

2. {prompt, time, festive}   {push, sing, late} _____ and _____

3. {crave, expect, consume}   {place, produce, eat} _____ and _____

4. {bend, flexible, strong}   {soft, rigid, fluid} _____ and _____

5. {quick, long, hasty}   {exit, fast, considered} _____ and _____

6. {obscure, quest, search}   {reveal, enquire, journey} _____ and _____

7. {defy, deny, save}   {rescue, admit, share} _____ and _____

8. {leave, together, gather}   {circle, apart, join} _____ and _____

EXTENSION Challenge task – Spotting the opposition

Pair up these tricky words by drawing lines to match them up. One is an odd one out! Ring it.

confine	miserly	contempt	liberate	dawdle
deposit	moist	withdraw	befuddle	respect
support	clarify	sabotage	hurry	generous

17 Complete the Sum

There are TWO types of questions for *Complete the Sum*:

▶ **Multiple choice:** You will have to choose a number from the options in order to complete the sum and make it accurate.

▶ **Open answer:** You will have to work out which number you need to complete the sum, before writing it out.

Top Tips

- If you enjoy mathematics, these are likely to be quick and easy.
- You will need to be able to add, subtract, multiply and divide with confidence.
- This is about finding the number that completes a sum, so both sides equal each other.
- Your first step is always to calculate the answer to the complete sum.
- This information is then used to calculate the missing number on the other side.
- Write out these sums to check your calculations.

Skills Practice   Basic operations

Try these simple starters, which will allow you to practise the basic operations of addition, subtraction, multiplication and division.

1.	Addition:	$22 + 9 = 18 + $ ▩	Missing number: _____
2.	Subtraction:	$100 - $ ▩ $= 85 - 35$	Missing number: _____
3.	Multiplication:	$6 \times 4 = 3 \times$ ▩	Missing number: _____
4.	Division:	$60 \div 2 = 120 \div$ ▩	Missing number: _____

TYPE 1 Multiple choice

Example: Which number do you need to complete the sum so it is correct?

28 + 31 = 32 + ▩

A) 28   **B)** 29   **C)** 27   **D)** 30

Answer: C. 28 + 31 = 59. 59 – 32 = 27. That means you need to add 27 to make it equal.

Which number do you need to complete the sum so it is correct?

1.   **17 + 9 =** ▩ **+ 14**

    A) 12   **B)** 14   **C)** 15   **D)** 13

2.   **72 + 18 = 83 +** ▩

    A) 12   **B)** 7   **C)** 8   **D)** 9

3.   **42 –** ▩ **= 25 + 8**

    A) 8   **B)** 11   **C)** 9   **D)** 10

4. $6 \times 11 = 100 -$ ▮

    A) 40   **B)** 38   **C)** 36   **D)** 34

5. $63 \div 9 =$ ▮ $- 11$

    A) 22   **B)** 14   **C)** 18   **D)** 20

6. $17 - 8 =$ ▮ $\times 3$

    A) 3   **B)** 4   **C)** 5   **D)** 6

7. $18 +$ ▮ $= 7 \times 6$

    A) 26   **B)** 28   **C)** 20   **D)** 24

8. ▮ $\times 8 = 80 - 16$

    A) 4   **B)** 8   **C)** 7   **D)** 6

9. $21 \div$ ▮ $= 84 \div 12$

    A) 6   **B)** 3   **C)** 4   **D)** 8

10. $14 + 13 = 42 -$ ▮

    A) 17   **B)** 19   **C)** 15   **D)** 14

TYPE 2 Open answer

Example: Complete this sum by adding the missing number.

         $81 \div$ ▮ $= 16 - 7$

Answer: 9. The answer is '9' as $16 - 7 = 9$ and 81 divided by 9 is also 9.

Complete these sums by identifying the missing numbers.

1. $8 + 14 = 44 \div$ ▮   **2.** $33 - 9 =$ ▮ $\times 8$

3. $14 + 25 = 72 -$ ▮   **4.** ▮ $\times 4 = 35 - 7$

5. ▮ $\div 7 = 19 - 12$ **6.** $16 + 40 = 8 \times$ ▮

7. $48 - 18 =$ ▮ $\times 6$ **8.** $88 \div$ ▮ $= 38 - 27$

9. ▮ $\times 12 = 50 - 2$ **10.** $21 \times 3 =$ ▮ $\times 7$

EXTENSION Challenge task – Tricky tripling

If you love mathematics and are finding these quite easy, try these three-stage sums.

1. $18 + 7 + 4 = 42 \div$ ▮ $+ 8$

2. $8 \times 3 \times 2 = 6 \times 12 -$ ▮

3. $50 \div 10 \times 12 = 8 \times 9 -$ ▮

4. $23 + 17 + 9 = 8 \times 6 +$ ▮

Now try matching the missing numbers to the sums and writing them out.

$8 \times 3 = 34 - ?$	11	$100 \div 20 = 55 \div ?$
9	$92 - 11 = 9 \times ?$	10

QUESTION TYPE 18 Related Numbers

There are TWO types of questions for *Related Numbers*:

▶ **Multiple choice:** You will have to calculate the operation by which numbers are related in two models. You should choose a number from the options which completes the related number sum in the same way.

▶ **Open answer:** You will have to work out which number you need to complete the related number sum before writing it out. There are no options, so it is vital that you work out the operation required in the first two models.

Top Tips

- ● These work in a similar way to Type 13, *Make a Word*.
- ● You are trying to work out the relationship between the numbers outside the brackets and the one in brackets.
- ● Once you have done this, you will have to do the same operation on a third model to find the missing number.
- ● You will need to use basic mathematics operations like addition, subtraction, multiplication and division.
- ● Your first step is always to calculate how the three numbers are related to each other in the first two models.
- ● Check both as it is possible that there is something which works for the first model, but not the second. It will not help you find the answer.

Skills Practice Working out relationships

Example: To do related numbers questions successfully, you have to identify the possible relationships between numbers, e.g.

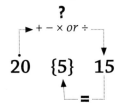

Here, if you subtract the second number from the first, you get the middle number.

Answer: The operation is 20 – 15 = 5.

Try some of these which use different mathematics operations. Write out the sum you need to do with the numbers OUTSIDE the bracket showing the number in brackets as the answer.

1. 42 {7} 6   Operation: _____

2. 18 {30} 12   Operation: _____

3. 16 {32} 48   Operation: _____

4. 9 {63} 7   Operation: _____

5. 32 {8} 4   Operation: _____

TYPE 1 Multiple choice

Example: Identify how the numbers are related in the first two models and pick the number which finishes the third in the same way.

  7 {21} 3   12 {96} 8   9 ▮ 6

  A) 45   **B)** 54   **C)** 78   **D)** 64

Answer: B. In the first two models, you multiply the numbers outside the brackets to calculate the one in the middle. Here, 9 × 6 = 54, so the answer is B.

Identify how the numbers are related in the first two models and pick the number which finishes the third in the same way.

1.	13 {3} 10 49 {32} 17 82 ▮ 14	**A)** 68 **B)** 70 **C)** 58 **D)** 96
2.	9 {63} 7 4 {96} 24 15 ▮ 7	**A)** 82 **B)** 100 **C)** 95 **D)** 105
3.	4 {5} 20 7 {7} 49 4 ▮ 128	**A)** 41 **B)** 25 **C)** 32 **D)** 28
4.	29 {54} 83 12 {65} 77 18 ▮ 67	**A)** 49 **B)** 52 **C)** 56 **D)** 17

TYPE 2 Open answer

Example: All of these are related in the same way. What is the missing number?

  4 {7} 28   5 {9} 45   6 ▮ 42

Answer: The answer is '7' as 42 ÷ 6 = 7.

Complete these sums by identifying the missing numbers.

1.	3 {12} 4	8 {72} 9	13 ▮ 6	**2.**	17 {19} 2 15 {32} 17 19 ▮ 26
3.	25 {3} 75	24 {4} 96	54 ▮ 216	**4.**	62 {48} 14 85 {64} 19 99 ▮ 37
5.	12 {132} 11	16 {144} 9	8 ▮ 18	**6.**	19 {14} 33 43 {29} 72 54 ▮ 119
7.	0.1 {1} 10	0.1 {10} 100	1 ▮ 1000	**8.**	11 {6} 66 13 {9} 97 17 ▮ 187
9.	25 {21} 4	42 {34} 8	53 ▮ 17	**10.**	14 {37} 23 103 {132} 29 54 ▮ 67

EXTENSION Challenge task – A double operation

These are operations which require two steps, so look carefully at the numbers to try to work out what is going on.

Try the first operation (+ − × or ÷) and then look at what you need to do to reach the number in brackets. You may need to add 1 or more, or times by a number.

1.	4 {27} 6	5 {53} 10	8 ▮ 2
2.	6 {7} 10	20 {25} 14	11 ▮ 8
3.	4 {8} 6	11 {33} 9	6 ▮ 12
4.	6 {100} 4	12 {200} 8	7 ▮ 9
5.	3 {63} 6	8 {48} 4	5 ▮ 7

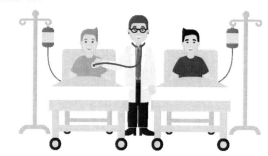

19 Word Number Codes

There are TWO types of questions for *Word Number Codes*:

▶ **Multiple choice:** You will have to match a code to one of the words listed or you might need to identify the code for a new word. Options will be given.

▶ **Open answer:** You will have to work out which words match which code writing them out. You may also be asked to encode or decode a new word which uses the letters given.

Top Tips

- For this code, numbers replace letters.
- Here, you will need to work out which number is code for each letter.
- This will let you identify the codes for particular words.
- You may also need to identify the code for new words which use the same letters.
- The order in which you solve these is key, so look for:
  — three-letter words;
  — words which share letters in the same position;
  — double letters;
  — two words which start and end with the same letter.
- Write out the code for each letter as you solve it, like A = 3 and use it to find the next letter, and so on.

Skills Practice Little steps

Unlike alphabet codes, these numbers are randomly assigned to letters, so the only clues are the other words and codes.

Example: **BOY   TOY   YET**

Their codes are: 823   623   346

The codes assigned are: B = 8, O = 2, Y = 3, T = 6, E = 4.

We can make more words out of these codes, so 846 is BET.

Here are three codes and three words.

321	RAT	435
EAT	135	AGE

Can you draw lines or highlight with different colours to show which one is the code for each word? If not, do these little steps to help:

- Do any number codes start or end with the same letter?
- If yes, find those two words. The third word is the other code.
- Now look at the third word and write out the code for each letter, as in Top Tips.
- Use these to work out the codes for the other two words.

TYPE 1 Multiple choice

Example: These words have all been given number codes.
Which one is RAT?

RAT   EAT   AGE   GET

A) 435   **B)** 321   **C)** 215   **D)** 135

Answer: A. RAT, EAT and GET all end in 5, so 321 is AGE.
This means 3 is A. 1 must be E, so 135 is EAT.
That means that 5 is T. RAT must be 435.

In each case, the codes are given for three words. Match them up and find the code for the new word out of the options given.

1. What is the code for SORE if these three codes are for these words? They are not in order.

   POST   SOAP   TEAR   1465   3762   5413

   A) 1625   **B)** 2731   **C)** 1427   **D)** 3714

2. What is the code for LOVE if these three codes are for these words? They are not in order.

   COME   MOVE   COIL   2165   4137   4125

   A) 7265   **B)** 7165   **C)** 5337   **D)** 6127

3. What is the code for MATE if these three codes are for these words? They are not in order.

   TIME   SAIL   LAST   2538   8527   7314

   A) 3284   **B)** 1325   **C)** 8314   **D)** 1574

4. What is the code for TAIL if these three codes are for these words? They are not in order.

   LOST   GOAT   TOIL   7324   4367   8357

   A) 7524   **B)** 8457   **C)** 4267   **D)** 4658

5. What is the code for REAP if these three codes are for these words? They are not in order.

   CARP   PIER   FACE   9245   5364   1296

   A) 4625   **B)** 5264   **C)** 6192   **D)** 4516

TYPE 2 Open answer

Example: Look at these codes and work out which one matches each word.
PEST   SAME   MICE   7412   9283   8572

Answer: SAME and MICE end in E, so E must be 2.
That means that PEST is 9283, so S is the 3rd letter and must be 8
SAME starts with S, so must be 8572. MICE must then be 7412.

Look at the following words and codes. One of the words does not have a code. See if you can match them up and answer the questions which follow.

CRAVE   VERSE   LEARN   SPARE   52782   17452   89472

1. Which word does not have a code?

2. What is the code for SPARE?

3. How would you write CARS in this code?

4. How would you write PRESS in this code?

5. What is the word behind the code 89247?

20 Complete the Word

There are TWO types of questions for *Complete the Word*:

▶ **Multiple choice:** You will have to work out the rule for the first two pairs of words and choose the word which completes this sequence.

▶ **Open answer:** You will have to work out the rule for the first two pairs of words and apply it to the third. This will give you a word which completes the sequence.

Top Tips

- You are given two pairs of words.
- The ones in brackets have been created from the first words in the same way, e.g. only using middle three letters.
- You need to work out how each word in the brackets has been made and do this to the final word to complete the brackets sequence.
- It will make a real word like the first two.
- The technique is similar to Type 13, *Make a Word*.

Skills Practice Same again

See if you can work out what the sequence is for some of these practice questions.

1. **sand (and)**   **boast (oast)**   **grace (_____)**

   Missing word: _____   Rule for sequence: _____

2. **fate (fat)**   **hate (hat)**   **pate (_____)**

   Missing word: _____   Rule for sequence: _____

3. **farm (farmer)**   **soon (sooner)**   **pray (_____)**

   Missing word: _____   Rule for sequence: _____

TYPE 1 Multiple choice

Example: Choose the word which should go in the final brackets to complete this sequence.

   sore (tore)   came (dame)   last (_____)

   ...j k ⓛ m n...

   A) stall   **B)** fast   **C)** mast   **D)** cast

Answer: C. You change the first letter of the first word. You use the next letter of the alphabet. 'Sore' becomes 'tore' and 'came' becomes 'dame'. To complete the sequence, 'last' becomes 'mast'.

As with *Make a Word*, you may need to number your letters in order, so you can rearrange in the same way.

Example: **flume (fuel)**   Numbers: 1352

Try numbering these:

1. glare (real)
2. gleam (male)
3. chore (ochre)

Example: Which word should be in the last brackets? Follow the same rule.

twice (ice)   **brink (ink)**   **slate (_____)**

A) late   **B)** eat   **C)** ate   **D)** salt

Answer: C. 'Ate' is the answer as it uses only the last three letters in consecutive order. 'Ice' uses the last three letters of 'twice' and 'ink' uses the last three letters of 'brink'.

Which word should be in the last brackets? Follow the same rule as for the first two.

4. **house (hose)**   **pound (pond)**   **bleed (_____)**
   A) bale   **B)** pole   **C)** bed   **D)** bled

5. **spore (rope)**   **store (rote)**   **lever (_____)**
   A) leer   **B)** ever   **C)** veer   **D)** love

6. **tramp (part)**   **leech (heel)**   **triad (_____)**
   A) trad   **B)** raid   **C)** dirt   **D)** tried

7. **dully (dummy)**   **sheet (shoot)**   **furry (_____)**
   A) fusty   **B)** firs   **C)** funny   **D)** rough

8. **throne (tone)**   **defame (dame)**   **strand (_____)**
   A) sand   **B)** stare   **C)** star   **D)** sad

TYPE 2 Open answer

Example: Which word is needed to complete the sequence?

stock (sock)   **brook (book)**   **dread (_____)**

Answer: The answer is 'dead' as you use the first letter, miss out the second and then use the final three letters.

Which word is needed to complete the sequence?

1. suite (site)   grape (gape)   soon (_____)
2. found (fund)   metal (meal)   latter (_____)
3. staple (tape)   crates (rats)   opened (_____)
4. bring (grin)   spins (spin)   panel (_____)
5. base (case)   gate (hate)   lead (_____)
6. early (year)   endow (wend)   eaten (_____)

EXTENSION Challenge task – Dismantling words

Look at these words and see if you can re-order ALL the letters to create new words.

1. carve *can be made into* _____   **Clue:** It means to want something.
2. endorse *can be made into* _____   **Clue:** These can fly.
3. plead *can be made into* _____   **Clue:** A bike needs these.
4. shore *can be made into* _____   **Clue:** An animal.
5. trace *can be made into* _____   **Clue:** It involves cooking for others.

QUESTION TYPE 21 | Same Meaning

There are TWO types of questions for *Same Meaning*:

) **Multiple meanings:** You will have to choose a word which goes equally well with two sets of words. You will be looking for a homograph, a word which is spelt the same but has two different meanings.

) **Open answer:** You will have to work out a word which can go with two sets of words. It will have a similar meaning to both sets of words, but will be spelt the same as it is a homograph.

Top Tips

- You are given two pairs of words.
- You need to find a word which will go equally well with both sets of words.
- The word will mean the same or be very similar to both sets of words.
- Cross out and eliminate obviously wrong answers.
- The answers are homographs which are spelt the same but mean different things, like 'watch' as a timepiece and 'to look at'.
- As you will see, the word may be a different word class for each pair of words: as a timepiece, 'watch' is a noun; as something you do, it is a verb.

Skills Practice Spot the ones leading double lives

Four of these words have double meanings. Can you ring or highlight these homographs? Crossing out wrong answers will help you find the homographs.

sad	boy	miss	light	selfish	garden
fine	car	festival	park	dark	curtain

These words can be two different word classes, like verbs, adjectives, nouns, etc. For each, write out two possible word classes.

1. tie Word classes: _____ and _____

2. absent Word classes: _____ and _____

3. frame Word classes: _____ and _____

TYPE 1 Multiple meanings

Example: Which option in brackets will go equally well with both pairs of words outside?
shore, beach (ocean, **coast**, rocks, cycle, wave) freewheel, glide

Answer: **coast**. 'coast' is a noun for the 'beach' and a verb meaning to 'glide' or 'freewheel'.

Look at these pairs of words. Ring, underline or highlight the options which will go equally well with both pairs?

1. pot, cup (**hit, pail, break, pan, mug**) attack, beat up
2. tiny, small (**minute, huge, watch, short, spell**) time, period
3. timber, pole (**dark, light, shadow, beam, torch**) glimmer, ray
4. point, score (**ambition, goal, match, game, team**) aim, target
5. twig, bough (**root, leaflet, branch, learn, stem**) subdivision, offshoot
6. blackout, giddy (**fast, ill, faint, well, pure**) faded, unclear
7. gale, blast (**strike, luck, blow, feel, wind**) upset, disaster
8. chief, main (**town, bank, capital, cash, credit**) money, wealth
9. rush, attack (**price, hasten, strike, charge, money**) cost, fee
10. fight, hit (**tin, punch, box, target, compete**) container, carton

TYPE 2 Open answer

These are much trickier when you do not have choices.

Take the pair most familiar to you and think of all the synonyms you can for these words. Try to see if any of these fit the second pair of words.

Example: Which word means the same as both these pairs of words? The first letter is 'b'.
      (**split, shatter**)   (**holiday, vacation**)   **Word: b** _____.

Answer: The answer is 'break' as this is a verb meaning to 'shatter' and also a noun for 'holiday'.

Find the homographs or words that mean the same as BOTH pairs of words.
The first letter is given.

1. (pole, column)   (letter, send)   p _____
2. (tick, right)   (fix, amend)   c _____
3. (brain, head)   (resent, dislike)   m _____
4. (attract, please)   (magic, spell)   c _____
5. (digit, number)   (form, shape)   f _____

EXTENSION Challenge task – Multiple meanings

Give the second meaning of these words.

1. **BILL** can mean an animal's beak.

   It can also mean _____.

2. **FAIR** can be a festival.

   It can also mean _____.

3. **PRESENT** can be a gift.

   It can also mean _____.

4. **BASS** can be a deep voice.

   It can also mean _____.

5. **NOVEL** can be a book.

   It can also mean _____.

FOCUS ON FAMILIES

As you start to become more familiar with the different types of Verbal Reasoning questions, you will notice that there are links between all of them, apart from **Type 15**, *Reading Information*.

This idea of links is helpful as you are using the **same skills** to tackle different question types. These can be seen as 'families.' Understanding one type can help you with another type.

Let us look at some of these families.

FAMILY 1 — Adding and Taking Away Letters

(Types 1 and 8)

For **Type 1** questions, *Insert a Letter*, you are given two incomplete words. ADDING a letter, which goes on the end of one word and beginning of another, will give you two complete words.

Example: Which letter will complete both words?

   gil   ale

Answer: Adding 'd' makes '**gild**' and '**dale**'.

For **Type 8** questions, *Move a Letter*, you are TAKING AWAY a letter from one word and ADDING it to another, again to create two words, new ones this time.

Example: Which letter can be taken from the first word and added to the second?

   flare   bind

Answer: If we take the 'l' from 'flare' and add it to 'bind', we get '**fare**' and '**blind**'.

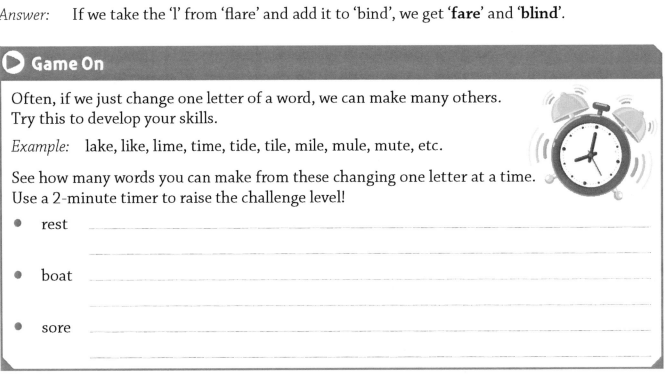

> **▶ Game On**
>
> Often, if we just change one letter of a word, we can make many others.
> Try this to develop your skills.
>
> *Example:*   lake, like, lime, time, tide, tile, mile, mule, mute, etc.
>
> See how many words you can make from these changing one letter at a time.
> Use a 2-minute timer to raise the challenge level!
>
> ●   rest ....
>
> ●   boat ....
>
> ●   sore ....

Where's the Word?

FAMILY 2

(Types 5, 6 and 12)

Types 5 and 6 are similar in terms of the skills you need.
You are looking for a missing 4 or 3-letter word.

In **Type 5**, *Hidden Words*, this word is 'hidden' between two words, so you need to look between each pair of words to find it.

Example: Find the 4-letter hidden word.

His mother bought him a jumper for Christmas.

Answer: The hidden word is **herb**, between 'mother' and 'bought'.

Type 6 questions, *Missing Words*, have an incomplete word in capitals. It needs a 3-letter word to finish it.

Example: Find the missing 3-letter word.

The archaeologist completed her EXPLOION of the mound.

Answer: A **RAT** is needed to make EXPLORATION.

For **Type 12** questions, *Compound Words*, you do not need to find a missing word, but do need to find two words that go together to make a new, compound word.

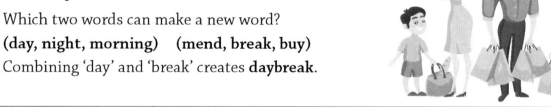

Example: Which two words can make a new word?

(day, night, morning)   (mend, break, buy)

Answer: Combining 'day' and 'break' creates **daybreak**.

▶ Game On

Give yourself: 1 point for every word you can make using the letters of 'establishment',
2 points for a compound word.

Remember to look for 2-letter words which make compound words like
in + *to* = **into**.

Use a timer or compete with a friend!

establishment

FAMILY 3 | Stirring it Up – Mixing the Letters

(Types 13 and 20)

These are similar types of questions as you have to mix up the letters to make new words. For both, you need to number the letters to work out how to rearrange them.

For **Type 13** questions, *Make a Word*, you have to make a word from a pair of words, by ordering the letters in the same way as another pair of words.

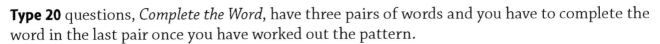

Example: Make the word in the second brackets in the same way as the first set.

mule (able) back   sink   atom

Answer: You should make the word *tank* using letters 6534.
Starting from 1, give a number to each letter OUTSIDE of the brackets.
So, m = 1, u = 2, l = 3, e = 4, b = 5, a = 6, c = 7 and k = 8.
able is numbers 6534.

Type 20 questions, *Complete the Word*, have three pairs of words and you have to complete the word in the last pair once you have worked out the pattern.

Example: Which word completes the sequence?

bland (band)   frame (fame)   store (   )

Answer: You complete with the word *sore* as you miss out the second letter of the first word.

▶ Game On

Take the word **throne**.
Let us see how many ways we can 'stir' up this word.
Number the word 123456 before you start (t = 1, h = 2, etc.).

- Remove the 1st three letters to create: _____

- Remove the 2nd and 3rd to create: _____

- Order the letters 1, 4, 3, 6 to create: _____

Think of other ways you can create words from '**throne**' or another word.

_____

_____

_____

_____

Nearest Relatives

FAMILY 4

(Types 2 and 10)

These questions are all about how words are related to each other.

Type 2 questions, *Related Words*, ask you to choose two words (out of 5) which are 'odd ones out'. The other three words will form a family. They could be: types of the same thing (e.g. buildings), synonyms, parts of the same object (eg. car parts), things that perform the same function (e.g. container), objects with same qualities (e.g. hot things), or any other word family.

You need to find a group of three words which are related and then spot the two 'odd ones out'. Be careful as the remaining two might be related to each other (though not to the other three). Look at this example.

Example: Which two words are not related to the others?
courgette parsnip carrot cabbage peas

Answer: 'parsnip' and 'carrot' are not related as the others are green. Also, these two are root vegetables and grow below the ground. As they were all vegetables, you had to find what else was different.

Type 10 questions, *Word Connections*, focus on how words are related and will ask you to complete a sentence, so you have two relationships which are the same.

Example: Which two words complete the sentence?
pupil is to (teacher, lazy, eye) as drum is to (ear, band, music)

Answer: 'ear' and 'drum'. This is tricky as pupil and drum are homographs (words which have multiple meanings). Here though, they are both parts of the body, so 'pupil is to eye as drum is to ear.' The relationship is 'part of' as in a 'pupil' is part of an 'eye' and a 'drum' is part of an 'ear'.

Look out for words which might confuse you like 'teacher' and 'band' in this question.

▶ Game On

Create a list of five words, three of which fit each category below and two which do not, but might trick someone into thinking they do.

Category	Related words (3 words)	Odd ones out (2 words)
Female animals		
Synonyms for 'excited'		
Professions		
Games played with a bat		

Same, Similar and Opposite

FAMILY 5

(Types 4, 16 and 21)

Three of the 21 types are about synonyms or antonyms, words with similar or opposite meanings.

Type 4 questions, *Closest Meaning*, ask you to select the two words which are closest in meaning. These are not always exact synonyms, but the words are 'closer' in meaning than any other pair of words available. Watch out for any antonyms.

Example: Select the two words which are closest in meaning.
                 liquid   fluid   solid   air   container

Answer: 'liquid' and 'fluid are closest in meaning.

Type 16 questions, *Opposite Meanings*, are about antonyms, so you need to choose two words most opposite in meaning, from two available groups of words. You should try each in turn, in order, to find the 'most' opposite. Watch out for any synonyms.

Example: Which two words are most opposite in meaning?
                 (opponent, army, resist)   (foe, ally, force)

Answer: 'opponent' and 'ally' are antonyms.
                 You need one from each set of brackets.
                 There were two pairs of synonyms here
                 which could have 'tripped' you up:
                 'opponent' and 'foe'; 'resist' and 'force'.

Type 21 questions, *Same Meaning*, are where you have to find a homograph, a word which is spelt the same, but has two different meanings. You are given synonyms for each 'meaning' to help you work it out.

Example: Which word fits with both pairs of words?
                 (penalty, fee)   (worthy, admirable)

Answer: 'fine'
                 'fine' is a noun for a charge and synonyms are 'penalty' and 'fee'. It is also an adjective
                 which can be replaced by synonyms like 'worthy' and 'admirable'.

Synonym and antonym questions need lots of practice as you will then find that you keep seeing the same or similar words, which will help you expand your vocabulary. Verbal Reasoning questions include complex and sophisticated vocabulary to test your understanding. Because of this, any activity which expands your vocabulary is useful.

The best thing you can do is read challenging books.

Other helpful tips:

- Use a dictionary to look up words you do not know when reading books.
- Look up synonyms for words when you are writing so you can practise using higher-level words. This will help with any writing tasks as well.

> ## ▶ Game On

Use a thesaurus to help you find synonyms and antonyms for each of these over-used emotion words. They are all adjectives.

Emotion	Synonyms	Antonyms
sad		
shy		
afraid		
bored		
confused		
energetic		

If you are looking for 'closest' meaning, you may find more than one synonym. It is important to realise that synonyms do not all equal the same level of something.

Consider the following synonyms for happy, which get progressively 'happier'!

glad   upbeat   amused   happy   delighted   exhilarated   elated   delirious

Clearly, 'exhilarated' and 'elated' are closer in meaning than 'glad' and 'exhilarated' as the emotion gets stronger. Not all synonyms are equal.

FAMILY 6 — The Numbers Game
(Types 7, 11, 17 and 18)

Verbal Reasoning questions require problem-solving skills, the ability to identify patterns and sequences and the manipulation of words, letters and numbers. For this reason, some of the questions include numbers, sometimes with letter codes and, at other times, much like conventional mathematics tasks.

Type 7 questions, *Letters for Numbers*, ask you to complete sums, but record the answers as letters. This is a form of code. As long as you read instructions carefully, these are normally not too hard, and so are quick to do. You may need to add, subtract, multiply or divide.

Example: A = 3   B = 7   C = 2   D = 5   E = 9
Write the answer to this sum as a letter: **E − B + A =**   .

Answer: D. The sum is 9 − 7 + 3 = 5   D

For **Type 11** questions, *Number Series*, you are asked to fill in a gap in a series of numbers. This depends on you working out how the sequence is created.

Example: Fill in the missing number in this series: **12   24   48   192**

Answer: 96. You double the number each time.

Type 17 questions ask you to *Complete the Sum*, where you are asked to identify or select a number which will balance out two halves of a sum. You write these answers as numbers. As before, you may need to add, subtract, multiply or divide.

Example: Complete the sum by filling in the missing number: **15 × 5 = 100 −**

Answer: **25**: 15 × 5 = 75; 100 − 25 = 75

Finally, **Type 18** questions, are *Related Numbers*, which work like Type 13, *Make a Word*. Here you have to work out the relationship between two numbers outside of brackets and the one inside. Instead of words, these use numbers and mathematics operations.
Complete the sum with the missing number.

Example: Work out how these are related and complete the last sum.
14 {40} 26   19 {36} 17   23 {   } 39

Answer: 62. The number in brackets is determined by adding the two numbers outside, so 23 + 39 = 62.

For numbers questions, you need to be adept at all mathematics operations – addition, subtraction, multiplication, division. Work out answers carefully as multiple choice answers often have numbers which are close to each other like 62, 61 and 64.

▶ Game On

See if you can work out which basic operation is missing in these sums.
Choose from +, −, × and ÷. Work out the complete sum first.
Do operations only in the order they appear, not BODMAS.

8   5 = 20 × 2   72   9 = 4 × 4 ÷ 2

37   12 = 4 + 1 × 5   14   4 = 49 ÷ 7 + 11

Alphabet Codes

(Types 3, 9, 14 and 19)

There are four question types which require you to have an alphabet at hand to help you complete them. There is always a copy in any Verbal Reasoning examination, but you might also want to write out an alphabet backwards for reasons which will become clear.

With alphabet code questions, it is important to think of the letters as numbers, as often a question merely requires you to add or subtract letters, which is why you need an alphabet handy, particularly a backward one for subtraction (unless you know your alphabet back-to-front).

Type 3 questions, *Word-Letter Codes*, require you to treat the alphabet as a secret, coding system, where you substitute one letter for another following a deliberate pattern such as adding two letters each time, so A becomes C, B becomes D, etc. These questions ask you to work out the pattern and use it to encode and decode words.

Encoding is turning a word into a code.

Example: **A B C D E F G H I J K L M**
N O P Q R S T U V W X Y Z
If the code for DOG is GRJ, what is the code for CAT?

Answer: FDW
To get from D to G, we add three letters (EFG); from O to R, we add three letters (PQR) and the same from G to J (HIJ). The code is +3 each time.

Decoding is unscrambling letters to find the original word.

Example: If BNEEDD is the code for COFFEE, what is SDZ?

Answer: TEA
To get from B to C, N to O, etc, we add one. The code is +1 each time.
However, you might be asked to work out the code for TEA, from the first part of the question. If so, you need to do this in REVERSE, so T would become S, E would become D and A would become Z.

It is vital to read questions carefully. The principle of treating letters like numbers extends to other CODE questions.

Type 9 questions, *Letter Series*, are like *Number Series* (Type 11) treating letters of the alphabet as numbers. You work out the number you add or subtract and continue the series.

Example: **A B C D E F G H I J K L M N O P Q R S T U V W X Y Z**
Which pair of letters come next in this series?
FS   HQ   JO   LM

Answer: NK
Treat each letter separately as you do for *Word-Letter Codes* (above).
Work out the first sequence, from F to H to J to L. This is +2, so L + 2 = N.
The next sequence is S to Q to O to M. This is −2, so M − 2 = K.

53

Type 14 questions, *Letter Connections*, are very similar to Type 9, as you have to work out the sequences of pairs of letters. These are expressed as a relationship or connection.

Example: **A B C D E F G H I J K L M N O P Q R S T U V W X Y Z**

Complete this sentence so it makes sense.

LK is to OO as FR is to   .

Answer: IV

As before, work out the first sequence, L to O. This is +3, so F becomes I.
The next sequence is K to O, which is +4. R + 4 = V.

Type 19 questions, *Word Number Codes*, work in a slightly different way as the coding is random. The challenge here is to work out which number is equivalent to which letter.

Example: There are three number codes and four words here. What is the code for MADE?

LAID   DAME   MADE   DEAL

7341   8473   1457

Answer: The code for MADE is 8473.

There are many ways to work this out. This is one:

- There are not two number sequences starting with the same code, for D, so either DEAL or DAME is not there.
- Three words have A as the second letter, so 4 must be A.
- 7341 has to be DEAL as it is the only one with a different second letter and A (4) as a third letter.
- DEAL must be 7341, so 7 is D, 3 is E and 1 is L.
- MADE is therefore M473. M must be 8.

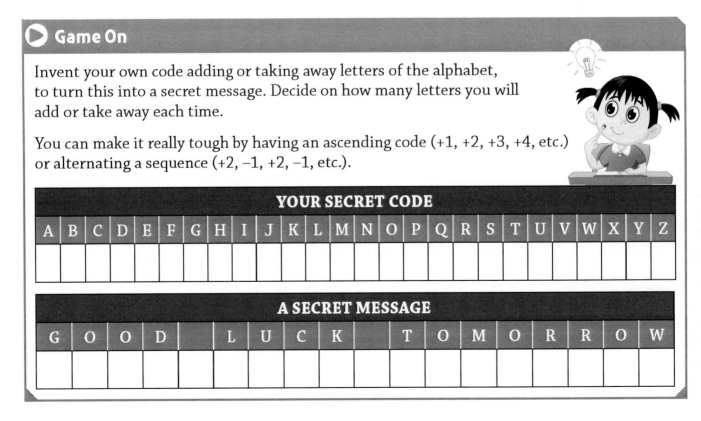

▶ Game On

Invent your own code adding or taking away letters of the alphabet, to turn this into a secret message. Decide on how many letters you will add or take away each time.

You can make it really tough by having an ascending code (+1, +2, +3, +4, etc.) or alternating a sequence (+2, −1, +2, −1, etc.).

YOUR SECRET CODE																									
A	B	C	D	E	F	G	H	I	J	K	L	M	N	O	P	Q	R	S	T	U	V	W	X	Y	Z

A SECRET MESSAGE														
G	O	O	D		L	U	C	K		T	O	M	O	R	R	O	W

VERBAL REASONING PAPERS

Advice and practical tips

During any Verbal Reasoning exam, there are some strategies which you can use to help minimise errors and to give yourself the best possible chance of showing what you can do.

Timing

For Verbal Reasoning, timing is crucial as you are often required to do each question in under a minute. Because of this, it is good to have a strategy like the one below.

- Firstly, do the question types you can do easily and quickly – get to the end of the paper.
- Then, go back and do the question types which you can do, but which take a little longer.
- Finally, do the ones you find hard or which you know can take a long time.

For multiple-choice answers, put a mark against EVERY question as you have a one in four, or five chance of getting it right.

As these are Practice Papers, you can approach the timing as you wish: if you have not done many papers, then just take your time to complete them all; if you are familiar with all the types, do the paper in 25 minutes, mark where you got up to and then complete it. For the next paper, do the same, and so on, to see if you can get faster with practice.

Reading questions

Read every question very carefully, as many errors are 'rubric' ones, where students misread the question.

The question might ask you to:
- select ONE **or** TWO options;
- identify something which is True **or** False;
- select from multiple-choice options;
- find a synonym **or** an antonym.

Rough work/working out

These questions benefit from working out on paper:
- **Codes:** Use the alphabet carefully for coding questions. Write the alphabet out backwards as well to help you. Write out words and codes before marking them on the paper.
- **Missing words:** Check the spelling of the word in capitals;
- **Make a word:** Write out the number order of the two words outside of the brackets and also check your answer is a proper word;
- **Numbers:** Do your working out on paper if mental mathematics is too hard, or if there are multiple operations;
- **Reading information:** Use charts, lists of timings, diagrams etc. for these as they involve dense and complex information. If you make a chart, use vertical and horizontal lines, so you do not make an error.

Verbal Reasoning Practice Paper 1

You have 25 minutes to complete all 12 question types.

QUESTION 1
Identify a letter which will complete all four words.

1.1 spor (   ) lder   acut (   ) lect

1.2 wido (   ) ring   allo (   ) atch

1.3 stea (   ) elon   pris (   ) eant

QUESTION 2
Underline, ring or highlight the two words not related to the other words.

2.1 A) trousers   **B)** skirt   **C)** blouse   **D)** jumper   **E)** shorts

2.2 A) sprint   **B)** dash   **C)** leap   **D)** hurdle   **E)** vault

2.3 A) bouquet   **B)** melody   **C)** choir   **D)** sheep   **E)** flock

QUESTION 3
Underline, ring or highlight the two words which are closest in meaning.

3.1 A) fearless   **B)** cold   **C)** bold   **D)** shy   **E)** climb

3.2 A) temper   **B)** annoyance   **C)** disrupt   **D)** irritation   **E)** infection

3.3 A) boy   **B)** adult   **C)** baby   **D)** teenager   **E)** infant

QUESTION 4
In every sentence, between two of the words, there is a hidden four-letter word. Find the word and write it out.

4.1 A full moon will occur every calendar month.   Hidden word: _____

4.2 The sixth inspection of the site revealed a cave.   Hidden word: _____

4.3 Eli loved getting computer games as presents.   Hidden word: _____

QUESTION 5
Write out the answers to these sums as letters.

5.1 A = 8,   B = 7,   C = 40,   D = 26,   E = 2 $C - D \div E =$ _____

5.2 A = 15,   B = 20,   C = 5,   D = 30,   E = 50 $E - A - C + B =$ _____

5.3 A = 100,   B = 1,   C = 10,   D = 0.1,   E = 1000 $E \div A =$ _____

QUESTION 6
Use the alphabet to work out these codes and words.

A B C D E F G H I J K L M N O P Q R S T U V W X Y Z

6.1 If the code for COLD is GSPH, what is the code for HOT? _____

6.2 If the code for SPACE is PMXZB, what is the code for ROCKET? _____

6.3 If LKQK is the code for KING, what does UJUSSK mean? _____

QUESTION 7
Complete the sentence so that it makes sense.

A B C D E F G H I J K L M N O P Q R S T U V W X Y Z

7.1 FJ is to HM as PH is to (   )

7.2 SB is to QX as LE is (   )

7.3 CA is to XZ as LM is to (   )

QUESTION 8
Make the word in the second brackets in the same way the first is made.

8.1 neat (sand) sold   atop (_____) glut

8.2 malt (mean) bend   salt (_____) fork

8.3 into (nice) cell   omen (_____) stir

QUESTION 9
Complete the sum by adding the missing number.

9.1 $83 - 17 = 54 +$

9.2 $8 \times 15 = 6 \times$

9.3 $72 \div 3 = 39 -$

QUESTION 10
Ring, underline or highlight the word which will go equally well with both sets of words.

10.1 tool, instrument (**cut, saw, blade, perceive**) glimpse, notice

10.2 agreement, understanding (**combine, promise, contract, accept**) shorten, abbreviate

10.3 company, organisation (**office, place, safe, firm**) solid, secure

QUESTION 11
Which TWO words can you make by moving one letter from the first to the second word?

11.1 shame   tank   _____ and _____

11.2 found   cast   _____ and _____

11.3 bread   tend   _____ and _____

QUESTION 12
Read the information and answer the questions.

> Four children go on a sponsored walk to raise money for charity. Bella raises £32.50, which is £13.60 less than Randall. Randall raises twice as much as Elliot, whilst Lana raises £19.50 more than Elliot makes.

12.1 Who raises the most money for charity? _____

12.2 How much money does Elliot raise? _____

Verbal Reasoning Practice Paper 2

You have 25 minutes to complete all 12 question types.

QUESTION 1
Ring, underline or highlight the three-letter word which will complete the word in capitals.

1.1 Cody had to watch his sugar levels as he was DIAIC.   (BAN, BIT, BET, MEN)

1.2 Joe was NIEEN today, the last year of his teens.   (NIT, NET, TEN, TAN)

1.3 There are twenty-one CONANTS in the alphabet.   (TON, RAN, LOT, SON)

QUESTION 2
Which letter do you need to move from the first word to make two different words?

2.1 shave	treat	**A)** s	**B)** h	**C)** v	**D)** e
2.2 clamp	fight	**A)** c	**B)** m	**C)** l	**D)** p
2.3 grown	diver	**A)** r	**B)** g	**C)** n	**D)** w

QUESTION 3
Complete the letter series by adding the next pair of letters.

A B C D E F G H I J K L M N O P Q R S T U V W X Y Z

3.1 AT   FR   KP   PN

3.2 VL   RM   NO   JR

3.3 DQ   BP   ZO   XN

QUESTION 4
Ring, underline or highlight the two words do you need to complete the sentence.

4.1 Lion is to (cat, cub, roar) as elephant is to (cow, trunk, calf).

4.2 Freedom is to (release, liberty, captivity) as creation is to (universe, destruction, art).

4.3 Bury is to (dead, dirt, berry) as made is to (do, mind, maid).

QUESTION 5
Complete the number series by adding the missing number.

5.1 4   9   36

5.2 87   78   69

5.3 10   0.1   0.01

QUESTION 6
Ring, underline or highlight the two words most opposite in meaning, one from each set.

6.1 (miserable, prosperous, deliberate)   (excellent, precious, poor)

6.2 (ignite, interrupt, exclude)   (endeavour, extinguish, elevate)

6.3 (praise, dignity, insult)   (complement, reward, compliment)

QUESTION 7

Identify how the numbers are related in the first two, and then fill in the missing number.

7.1 68 {51} 17   39 {21} 18   72 {   } 28

7.2 16 {64} 4   12 {132} 11   18 {   } 7

7.3 9 {360} 4   17{850} 5   9 {   } 9

QUESTION 8

Identify how you make the words in brackets in the first two, and then fill in the final word.

8.1 scare (scar)   brand (bran)   cover (_____)

8.2 lucky (yuck)   mint (tin)   tired (_____)

8.3 loan (moan)   meat (neat)   sense (_____)

QUESTION 9

Read the information and answer the questions.

Faiza has three hamsters, a poodle and a cat. Her friend, Lee, has three cats, a gerbil and two snakes, while their neighbour, Amber, has one less cat than Lee, a pug, and one more hamster than Faiza. Ray only has a horse, but his sister, Celia has a German Shepherd, a tortoise and two cats.

9.1 Which person or family has the most pets?   _____

9.2 How many rodents do the children have between them?   _____

9.3 Who has the second least number of pets, after Ray?   _____

QUESTION 10

Look at the following words and codes which are not in order. One word has no code.
Work out which code belongs to which word in order to answer the questions.

STRONG   GROPES   PRONGS   POSTER
523479   349216   692573

10.1 What does 523479 mean?   _____

10.2 How would you write SORT?   _____

10.3 What does the code 9237 mean?   _____

QUESTION 11

Insert a letter to complete all four words.

11.1 exce (   ) egal   vita (   ) ease

11.2 shel (   ) lock   aloo (   ) lute

11.3 slan (   ) lare   shru (   ) nome

QUESTION 12

Which TWO words contain the hidden, four-letter word? It ends one word and starts the next.

12.1 The crab leaned in and bit her left toe.   _____ and _____

12.2 His mother was a cardiac heart specialist.   _____ and _____

Verbal Reasoning Practice Paper 3

You have 25 minutes to complete all 12 question types.

QUESTION 1
Ring, underline or highlight the two words which are not related to the other three.

1.1 endure, educate, instruct, condemn, coach   **1.2** lobster, crab, cod, prawn, sea

1.3 bull, cockerel, hen, sow, stallion

QUESTION 2
Find and write out the four-letter word hidden in each sentence.

2.1 The boss asked me to circulate the update among staff.   Word: _____

2.2 Although the leg ached, the reflex itself seemed fine.   Word: _____

2.3 She had an apple and an orange for breaktime snack.   Word: _____

QUESTION 3
Which pair of letters should be next in this series? Select one of the options.

A B C D E F G H I J K L M N O P Q R S T U V W X Y Z

3.1 XL	YJ	ZH	AF	**A)** BE	**B)** ZD	**C)** BD	**D)** WG
3.2 EP	JR	OT	TV	**A)** ZX	**B)** XY	**C)** VW	**D)** YX
3.3 RK	QL	OM	LN	**A)** HO	**B)** SL	**C)** RP	**D)** IO

QUESTION 4
Which word should go in the second set of brackets? Make it the same way as the first set.

4.1 ours (lout) slit   grip (_____) hole

4.2 game (team) tile   rote (_____) bail

4.3 espy (sale) heal   yard (_____) bill

QUESTION 5
Ring, underline or highlight two words, one from each bracket, that make a compound word?

5.1 (grasp, know, learn)   (peak, heap, ledge)   **5.2** (sheep, ewe, ram)   (line, page, note)

5.3 (fact, true, sure)   (on, love, or)

QUESTION 6
Identify the sequence to complete the number series and fill in the gap.

6.1 448 224 112 ___ 28   **6.2** 27 36 45 54 ___   **6.3** 10 20 ___ 70 110

QUESTION 7
Work out the code in order to solve these.

A B C D E F G H I J K L M N O P Q R S T U V W X Y Z

7.1 If the code for SUNNY is TWQRD, what is the code for STORM? _____

7.2 If the code for GIFT is KMJX, what is the code for PRESENT? _____

7.3 A coding system makes CIRCLE into AGPAJC. What is IGRC?

QUESTION 8
Move one letter from the first to the second word. Which two new words are made?

8.1 left   reuse   _____ and _____

8.2 baulk   hunt   _____ and _____

8.3 exist   wore   _____ and _____

QUESTION 9
Read the information and answer the questions.

> Five friends agreed to meet at Gatwick to catch a flight for their holiday. The flight was due to leave at 16.10. In order to catch it, they needed to have completed booking in 30 minutes before this. George arrived at 15.20 and it took him 15 minutes to complete booking in. Samir and Sanuvi arrived 10 minutes later, with booking in only taking 10 minutes. Boris had 'Priority Booking' which meant he could arrive 15 minutes after the normal booking in deadline and board immediately – he got to the airport at 15.50. When Lenita arrived to book in, it was 15 minutes after Samir and Sanuvi had arrived.

9.1 Who, if anyone, missed the flight? ....

9.2 Who was ready first to board the plane? ....

9.3 What time did Samir and Sanuvi complete booking in? ....

QUESTION 10
Which pair of words are closest in meaning?

10.1 credible   suitable   believable   visible

    A) credible and suitable   **B)** believable and visible

    C) credible and believable   **D)** suitable and believable

10.2 dessert   desert   expose   abandon

    A) dessert and desert   **B)** desert and abandon

    C) expose and desert   **D)** abandon and expose

10.3 crop   grow   cultivate   plough

    A) grow and cultivate   **B)** plough and crop

    C) crop and cultivate   **D)** grow and plough

QUESTION 11
Complete the word which means the same as both pairs of words. The first letter is given.

11.1 (tiny, little)   (time, unit)   m _____

11.2 (greeting, goodbye)   (surf, sea)   w _____

11.3 (coach, teach)   (transport, rail)   t _____

QUESTION 12
Write the answer to the sum as a letter.

12.1 A = 6   B = 2   C = 21   D = 24   E = 7 $E \times A \div B = $ _____

12.2 A = 4   B = 3   C = 2   D = 6   E = 8 $E - C \times B \div B = $ _____

Verbal Reasoning Practice Paper 4

You have 25 minutes to complete all 12 question types.

QUESTION 1
Which two words are not related to the others? Select both words.

1.1 A) gold **B)** mercury **C)** silver **D)** platinum **E)** copper

1.2 A) trumpet **B)** trombone **C)** guitar **D)** violin **E)** saxophone

1.3 A) delicious **B)** unique **C)** exceptional **D)** evidence **E)** uncommon

QUESTION 2
Find the four-letter word hidden between two words and write it out.

2.1 His son's creche remained open until seven each day.   Word: _____

2.2 Being scouted was her main chance to get into the team.   Word: _____

2.3 Some people have illnesses without symptoms.   Word: _____

QUESTION 3
A missing three-letter word will complete the word in capitals. What is it?

3.1 He found it really AWKD meeting his girlfriend's family.   Word: _____

3.2 The teacher RECOMDED a good revision guide.   Word: _____

3.3 Their aunt decided to ACCOMY them on a walk.   Word: _____

QUESTION 4
Choose the correct two words to complete the sentence – show the same word connection.

4.1 Judge is to (crime, court, law) as pharmacist is to (mind, tablet, chemists).

4.2 Store is to (place, cupboard, story), as unite is to (together, unity, team).

4.3 Protect is to (help, harm, cover) as frail is to (success, strange, strong).

QUESTION 5
Which option CANNOT be combined with the first word to make a compound word?

5.1 BACK **A)** STIR **B)** DATE **C)** PACK **D)** LOG

5.2 TIME **A)** SOME **B)** WAR **C)** LAST **D)** ANY

5.3 EYE **A)** BALL **B)** LASH **C)** DROP **D)** MAKE

QUESTION 6
Complete the letter series by adding the next pair of letters.

A B C D E F G H I J K L M N O P Q R S T U V W X Y Z

6.1 BR CQ EP HO _____

6.2 TS UU VW WY _____

6.3 JW MU PS SQ _____

QUESTION 7
Read the information closely and answer the questions which follow.

> On the summer camp, the children got to choose their activities for the week. Craig opted for three of the choices, but not archery. Tala did canoeing and zip wire while Pixie opted for two, not including nature trail nor canoeing. Ralf did the same as Craig, except he did archery as well.

7.1 Which activity did all children do?

7.2 Who did the nature trail?

7.3 Which was the second most popular activity?

QUESTION 8
Select the word which is most opposite in meaning to the first word.

8.1 success   **A)** achieve   **B)** prize   **C)** failure   **D)** challenge

8.2 educated   **A)** intelligent   **B)** beginner   **C)** learner   **D)** ignorant

8.3 against   **A)** for   **B)** stand   **C)** under   **D)** over

QUESTION 9
Which number will complete the sum?

9.1 $75 \div 5 + 17 = 8 \times$ ____   **A)** 6   **B)** 4   **C)** 5   **D)** 3

9.2 $42 -$ ____ $= 8 \times 3$ **A)** 19   **B)** 14   **C)** 16   **D)** 18

9.3 $99 + 13 =$ ____ $\div 4 - 13$ **A)** 500   **B)** 360   **C)** 480   **D)** 720

QUESTION 10
Match up the sample words and codes to answer these questions.

       FEAR   RISE   STAR   FAST   5729   5476   2976   6824

10.1 What is the code for FAST?

10.2 What will be the code for RIFE?

10.3 What will be the code for REST?

QUESTION 11
All of these groups of numbers are related in the same way. What is the missing number?

11.1 28 {7} 4   96 {12} 8   66 { ____ } 6

11.2 5 {300} 6   7 {630} 9   12 { ____ } 7

11.3 49 {76} 27   137 {212} 75   19 { ____ } 63

QUESTION 12
Insert a letter to complete all four words.

12.1 surve (____) east   vacanc (____) ield

12.2 plum (____) ledge   usur (____) ermit

ANSWERS

Verbal Reasoning Question Types

1 Insert a Letter (p. 4–5)

Multiple choice

1. C) h
2. D) t
3. B) w
4. C) m
5. B) o

Open answer

1. l
2. e
3. p
4. r
5. d
6. k
7. m
8. s
9. w
10. f

Extension

1. e, f — scare, east, scarf fast
2. g, d — bang, band, drew, grew
3. w, p — claw, clap, peak, weak

2 Related Words (p. 6–7)

Skills Practice

1. farm animals
2. winter weather
3. facial features / senses
4. synonyms for 'untidy'
5. outer wear

Multiple choice

1. A) and C) The others are verbs, synonyms of 'shut'.
2. B) and D) The rest are currency.
3. A) and E) The others refer to wood parts of a tree.
4. C) and E) The others are verbs meaning 'to persuade'.
5. A) and D) The others are verbs meaning 'to send'.

Open answer

1. face and draw
   The others refer to colour shades.
2. horse and trough
   The others are places where animals live.
3. nephew and father
   The others are female relatives.
4. road and rail
   The others are modes of transport.
5. seek and top
   The others are synonyms of 'to cover'.
6. dog and wolf
   The others are collective nouns.
7. artist and painting
   The others are verbs meaning 'to create'.
8. afterlife and grave
   The others are synonyms of 'ghost'.
9. tree and board
   The others are types of trees.
10. biography and drama
    The others are writers.

Extension

- **Red synonyms:** ruby, scarlet, cherry, vermilion
- **Small synonyms:** miniscule, minute, miniature, tiny, microscopic, compact
- **Organs:** spleen, lung, heart, bladder, liver
- **Flowers:** carnation, tulip, orchid, rose, lily

3 Word-Letter Codes (p. 8–9)

Encoding

1. FKLSV (+3)
2. QKCJJ (−2)
3. TQGC (+1, +2)
4. PMSR (+4)
5. CFD (−3)
6. IURVW (+3)
7. PYGL (−2)
8. TWNGT (+2)

Decoding

1. SQUARE (+1)
2. SAD (−5)
3. OVER (−2, −1)
4. PEARL (−3)
5. BARK (−1, −2, −3, −4)

Extension

Spy Message: We will attack the bridge from the west at midnight on January tenth.

4 Closest Meaning (p. 10–11)

Multiple choice

1. B) luminous
2. C) unruffled
3. D) fracture
4. B) demand
5. A) period
6. D) climb and ascend
7. B) original and authentic
8. C) bizarre and absurd

Open answer

1. bowl and basin
2. growl and snarl
3. sieve and strain
4. infuriated and enraged
5. skill and ability
6. grief and sorrow

Extension

relent and yield, cutlass and rapier, lenient and permissive, infinite and boundless, potent and powerful

5 Hidden Words (p. 12–13)

Multiple choice

1. D) scarf indoors (find)
2. B) very early (year)
3. C) for their (fort)
4. C) push other (shot)

Open answer

1. gone – hug one
2. each – he ached
3. cold – gigantic old
4. oven – love nothing
5. chat – each attempt
6. rest – were staying
7. edit – collected items
8. deep – rude episode
   OR odes – episode shocked
9. lord – local ordinary
10. neat – lone attack
11. mast – Emma stood
12. exam – complex amendments

Extension

1. veto (have too)   2. pang (keep anger)

6 Missing Word (p. 14–15)

Skills Practice

1. stu**den**t
2. **car**eless OR **car**eless
3. op**en**ing
4. ex**pan**d
5. at**ten**d
6. des**perate** OR des**per**ate

Multiple choice

1. B) AND
2. C) SPA
3. D) HIM
4. E) LET
5. C) POT
6. A) RAT

Open answer

1. RAN – RESTAURANT
2. OWN – FROWNED
3. BIT – INHABITANTS
4. SON – POISONOUS
5. HEN – COMPREHENSION
6. MAT – IMMATURE
7. TEN – MAINTENANCE
8. CAT – MULTIPLICATION
9. MEN – ENVIRONMENT
10. BUN – ABUNDANT

Extension

- DISHEARTENED – TEN
- CONTINUE – TIN
- MONOTONY – TON
- RECTANGLE – TAN

7 Letters for Numbers (p. 16–17)

Skills Practice

1. 24
2. 5
3. 15
4. 11
5. 8

Multiple choice

1. D) $4 + 6 - 2 = 8$
2. E) $7 \times 2 - 4 = 10$
3. B) $20 \times 5 - 50 = 50$
4. B) $12 + 2 + 4 - 2 = 16$
5. D) $15 + 17 - 19 = 13$

Open answer

1.	M (7)	**2.**	Y (6)
3.	S (36)	**4.**	F (16)
5.	N (4)	**6.**	82
7.	16	**8.**	50
9.	10	**10.**	210

Extension

C) $12 \times 8 \div 2 \div 4 - 8 = 4$

8   Move a Letter   (p. 18–19)

Skills Practice

1. r, d
2. t
3. l
4. c or u
5. u, r, t

Multiple choice

1. C) n   (glad, spend)
2. D) h   (wit, bath)
3. B) r   (bush, heart)
4. C) m   (lie, champ)
5. A) l   (sang, realm)
6. B) r   (gown, harm)
7. D) f   (rile, left)
8. A) u   (tape, bound)
9. B) o   (cast, course)
10. C) i   (pant, ruins)

Open answer

1. band and sport
2. tiled and salt
3. fend and genie
4. taster and shout
5. rain and stick
6. feat and waist
7. cold and pound
8. core and thorn
9. pose and claim
10. lever and pact

Extension

1. hue and badge
2. trope and proud

3. down and hearth
4. nave and waive
5. best and allay

9   Letter Series   (p. 20–21)

Skills Practice

1. L (+1, +2, +3, +4)
2. Z (+3)
3. I (–1)
4. L (+1, +2, +1, +2)

Multiple choice

1. B) TC (+1, –1)
2. D) LH (+2, +1)
3. B) WO (ascending +1, + 2, etc. then +1)
4. B) OJ (–2, –2)
5. A) FN (ascending +1, + 2, etc. then +1)

Open answer

1. VO (+2, –2)
2. UZ (ascending +1, +2, etc. and then –1)
3. TG (+3, –3)
4. AN (+1, +2)
5. KH (descending –5, –4, etc. then +1)
6. QX (+2, +2)
7. CJ (alternating +2, –1, etc. then +1)
8. VF (+3, –1)

Extension

1. T   2. W
3. J

10   Word Connections   (p. 22–23)

Skills Practice

- piglet and foal   baby animals
- plus and add   synonyms
- fridge and cold   fridge has the quality of cold
- play and football   you play football
- snake and lizard   types of reptiles

Multiple choice

1. B) organ, limb (is a)
2. B) garage, theatre (works in a)
3. A) guitar, piano (is used to play)

4. D) opaque, hinder (antonym)

5. C) 90, 300 (multiplied by 10)

Open answer

1. add, multiply (synonym)

2. country, continent (is part of a)

3. pig, elephant (female version)

4. summer, winter (when it happens)

5. musician, book (collective noun for)

6. medicine, construction (practises)

7. waste, wood (homophones)

8. flower, tree (is a type of)

9. bleat and roar (makes this noise)

10. post and send (how they are transferred)

11. touch and hear (function)

12. bump and sun (rhyme)

Extension

- architect – buildings
- accountant – figures
- archaeologist – ruins
- archivist – files
- astronaut – spacecraft

11 Number Series (p. 24–25)

Skills Practice

1. **Addition:** 16 (+2)

2. **Subtraction:** 25 (–5)

3. **Multiplication:** 32 (×2)

4. **Division:** 81 (÷ 3)

Multiple choice

1. B) 20 (+4)

2. D) 34 (–12)

3. A) 24 (+7)

4. B) 45 (+5, +10 alternating)

5. D) 72 (doubling)

Open answer

1. 80 (doubling)

2. 61 (–6)

3. 38 (+2, +4, +6, +8)

4. 0.01 (move one decimal place)

5. 65 (–15)

6. 11 (doubling)

7. 675 (–1 on each number)

8. 58 (–18)

9. 28 (–7)

10. 0.197 (move one decimal place)

Extension

1. 100 (squared numbers 10 × 10 = 100)

2. 216 (cubed numbers 6 × 6 × 6 = 216)

3. 400 (first, third and fifth numbers multiplying by 10 each time; second series is +3)

4. 18 (9-times table, 8-times table)

5. 10 (÷10, +5)

6. 6 (3-times table, 4-times table)

12 Compound Words (p. 26–27)

Skills Practice

- jellyfish
- suntan
- island
- snowball
- firestation

Multiple choice

1. C) playtime

2. B) headdress

3. A) fortnight

4. C) household

5. D) standstill

Open answer

1. landslide

2. passport

3. backstroke

4. heart

5. indeed

6. waterfall

7. legend

8. soundproof

9. wheelchair

10. overseas

Extension

1. fold (foothold, footfall, footlights)

2. rage (inform, inside, indoors)

3. sun (honeymoon, honeysuckle, honeycomb)

4. all can combine (landmark, island, landslide, landward)

13 Make a Word (p. 28–29)

Skills Practice

1. **A)** 5834 or 5234

    B) 8714   **C)** 8236

2. Possible words (other answers are possible):

A) wane or claw or wear or cone

B) made or fame or lead or self

C) fort or care or tear or core

D) meat or bare or roam or brag

Multiple choice

1. C) sane (5261) 2. A) drip (8164)

3. B) crew (1278)

4. D) sale (1625)

5. C) tank (6534)

Open answer

1. love (7814) 2. tail (5238)

3. iron (3256) 4. sand (3815)

5. beak (5274) 6. lamp (7351)

7. nose (3617) 8. fast (5238)

Extension

1. ALSO – FAIL and ROSE (2476)

2. GOLD – LEGS and MODE (3617)

3. CAKE – FACE and KITE (3258)

4. BEAR – MAKE and BORE (5427) or BEAR and VASE

5. STEP – VASE and PLOT (3845) or ROSE and PLOT

14 Letter Connections (p. 30–31)

Skills Practice

1. T (–2) 2. L (+5)

3. E (–5) 4. Y (mirror)

Multiple choice

1. B) FI (+2, –1) 2. D) JQ (–4, +2)

3. A) VM (+3, +2) 4. C) IL (+3, –2)

5. D) HL (–2, +3)

Open answer

1. IK (–1, –2) 2. TH (+4, +4)

3. FT (–2, –4) 4. CG (+5, +5)

5. GZ (–3, +1) 6. UO (+3, +3)

7. XW (Mirror) 8. QR (+6, +2)

Extension

1. HQ becomes 'it' (+1, +3)

2. RM becomes 'so' (+1, +2)

3. SN becomes 'to' (+1, +1))

15 Reading Information (p. 32–33)

Skills Practice

1. Johnny 2. Aya and Fred

3. Rifat

Multiple choice

1. C) John walks 100 miles.

2. B) Jo and Tamzy arrive at the same time.

Open answer

1. **A)** Monica **B)** 4th June

   C) No

   D) It is before 28th May.

2. **A)** 26 **B)** 35

   C) 47

16 Opposite Meaning (p. 34–35)

Skills Practice

- accept and reject
- deep and shallow
- profit and loss
- come and go
- help and hinder
- simple and elaborate

Multiple choice

1. C) humble and boastful

2. D) tired and energised

3. B) punish and reward

4. - **meagre**: enough
   - **decline**: accept
   - **idle**: active
   - **perish**: flourish
   - **advance**: retreat
   - **docile**: wild
   - **imitation**: original

Open answer

1. occupy and vacate

2. prompt and late

3. consume and produce

4. flexible and rigid

5. hasty and considered

6. obscure and reveal

7. deny and admit

8. together and apart

Extension

Odd one out = moist

- confine and liberate
- deposit and withdraw
- clarify and befuddle
- respect and contempt
- support and sabotage
- hurry and dawdle
- miserly and generous

17   Complete the Sum   (p. 36–37)

Skills Practice

1. 13
2. 50
3. 8
4. 4

Multiple choice

1. A) 12
2. B) 7
3. C) 9
4. D) 34
5. C) 18
6. A) 3
7. D) 24
8. B) 8
9. B) 3
10. C) 15

Open answer

1. 2
2. 3
3. 33
4. 7
5. 49
6. 7
7. 5
8. 8
9. 4
10. 9

Extension

1. 2
2. 24
3. 12
4. 1

Matching:

- $8 \times 3 = 34 - \mathbf{10}$
- $92 - 11 = 9 \times \mathbf{9}$
- $100 \div 20 = 55 \div \mathbf{11}$

18   Related Numbers   (p. 38–39)

Skills Practice

1. $42 \div 6 = 7$
2. $18 + 12 = 30$
3. $48 - 16 = 32$
4. $9 \times 7 = 63$
5. $32 \div 4 = 8$

Multiple choice

1. A) 68
2. D) 105
3. C) 32
4. A) 49

Open answer

1. 78
2. 45
3. 4
4. 62
5. 144
6. 65
7. 1000
8. 11
9. 36
10. 121

Extension

1. times, +3 = 19
2. add, −9 = 10
3. times, divide by 3 = 24
4. add, times 10 = 160
5. times second number by 10, add first = 75

19   Word Number Codes   (p. 40–41)

Skills Practice

- EAT = 135
- AGE = 321
- RAT = 435

Multiple choice

1. C) 1427
2. B) 7165
3. D) 1574
4. A) 7524
5. A) 4625

Open answer

1. LEARN
2. 89472
3. 1478
4. 97288
5. SPEAR

20 Complete the Word   (p. 42–43)

Skills Practice

1. race – remove the first letter.
2. pat – remove the last letter.
3. prayer – add 'er'.

Multiple choice

1. 4532
2. 5423
3. 31245
4. D) bled
5. B) ever
6. C) dirt
7. C) funny (change double consonant)
8. A) sand

Open answer

1. son
2. later
3. pend
4. lane
5. mead
6. neat

Extension

1. crave
2. drones
3. pedal
4. horse
5. cater

21 Same Meaning   (p. 44–45)

Skills Practice

1. fine, miss, light, part
2. A) verb and noun
   B) adjective and noun
   C) verb and noun

Multiple meanings

1. mug
2. minute
3. beam
4. goal
5. branch
6. faint
7. blow
8. capital
9. charge
10. box

Open answer

1. post
2. correct
3. mind
4. charm
5. figure

Extension

1. cost of something (noun)
2. just or right (adjective)
3. show, demonstrate (verb)
4. fish (noun)
5. new, different (adjective)

Verbal Reasoning Tests

Practice Paper 1 (p. 56–57)

1. **1.1** e – spore, elder, acute, elect
    1.2 w – widow, wring, allow, watch
    1.3 m – steam, melon, prism, meant
2. **2.1** blouse and jumper – others are bottoms
    2.2 sprint and dash – others are jumps
    2.3 melody and sheep – rest are collective nouns
3. **3.1** bold and fearless
    3.2 annoyance and irritation
    3.3 infant and baby
4. **4.1** cure (occur every)
    4.2 thin (sixth inspection)
    4.3 edge (loved getting)
5. **5.1** B (7)
    5.2 E (50)
    5.3 C (10)
6. **6.1** LSX (+4)
    6.2 OLZHBQ (–3)
    6.3 THRONE (–1, –2, –3)
7. **7.1** RK (+2, +3)
    7.2 JA (–2, –4)
    7.3 ON (mirror)
8. **8.1** goat
    8.2 soar
    8.3 most
9. **9.1** 12
    9.2 20
    9.3 15
10. **10.1** saw
    10.2 contract
    10.3 firm
11. **11.1** same and thank (h)
    11.2 fund and coast (o)
    11.3 bead and trend (r)
12. **12.1** Randall
    12.2 £23.05

Practice Paper 2 (p. 58–59)

1. **1.1** BET   **1.2** NET
    1.2 SON
2. **2.1** h (save and threat) or s (have and treats)
    2.2 l (camp and flight)
    2.3 r (gown and driver)
3. **3.1** UL (+5, –2)
    3.2 FV (–4, then +1, +2 ascending)
    3.3 VM (–2, –1)
4. **4.1** cub, calf (baby animals)
    4.2 captivity, destruction (antonyms)
    4.3 berry, maid (homophones)
5. **5.1** 25 (squared numbers)
    5.2 60 (–9)
    5.3 1 (move decimal point)
6. **6.1** prosperous and poor
    6.2 ignite and extinguish
    6.3 insult and compliment
7. **7.1** 44 (subtraction)
    7.2 126 (multiply)
    7.3 810 (multiply, times by 10)
8. **8.1** cove (remove last letter)
    8.2 dire (remove 1st letter, replace with last)
    8.3 tense (use next letter of alphabet at start)
9. **9.1** Amber
    9.2 8 (hamsters and gerbils)
    9.3 Celia (4)
10. **10.1** POSTER   **10.2** 3294
    10.3 ROSE
11. **11.1** l (excel, legal, vital, lease)
    11.2 f (shelf, flock, aloof, flute)
    11.3 g (slang, glare, shrug, gnome)
12. **12.1** crab leaned (able)
    12.2 cardiac heart (ache)

Practice Paper 3 (p. 60–61)

1. **1.1** endure and condemn – rest synonyms for 'teach'
   1.2 cod and sea – rest are shellfish
   1.3 sow and hen – rest are male animals

2. **2.1** team (update among)
   2.2 exit (reflex itself) or here (the reflex)
   2.3 lean (apple and)

3. **3.1** C – BD (+1, –2)
   3.2 D – YX (+5, +2)
   3.3 A – HO (–1,–2, –3, etc, then +1)

4. **4.1** ogre (6128)
   4.2 blot (5823)
   4.3 ally (2781)

5. **5.1** knowledge
   5.2 rampage
   5.3 factor

6. **6.1** 56 (halve)
   6.2 63 (9 × table)
   6.3 40 (+10, +20, +30, etc.)

7. **7.1** TVRVR (+1, +2 ascending)
   7.2 TVIWIRX (+4)
   7.3 KITE (+2)

8. **8.1** let and refuse (f)
   8.2 bulk and haunt (a)
   8.3 exit and worse (s)or exit and swore (s)

9. **9.1** Lenita
   9.2 George
   9.3 15.40

10. **10.1** C – credible and believable
    10.2 B – desert and abandon
    10.3 A – grow and cultivate

11. **11.1** minute
    11.2 wave
    11.3 train

12. **12.1** C – 21
    12.2 D – 6

Practice Paper 4 (p. 62–63)

1. **1.1** B + E (not precious metals)
   1.2 C +D (not brass instruments)
   1.3 A + D (does not mean 'rare')

2. **2.1** here (creche remained)
   2.2 inch (main chance) OR tint (get into)
   2.3 veil (have illnesses)

3. **3.1** WAR (AWKWARD)
   3.2 MEN (RECOMMENDED)
   3.3 PAN (ACCOMPANY)

4. **4.1** court, chemists (where work)
   4.2 story, unity (change e to y)
   4.3 harm, strong (antonyms)

5. **5.1** A – STIR
   5.2 C – LAST
   5.3 D – MAKE

6. **6.1** LN (+2, +3 ascending, –1)
   6.2 XA (+1, +2)
   6.3 VO (+3, –2)

7. **7.1** zip wire
   7.2 Craig and Ralf
   7.3 canoing (3)

8. **8.1** C – failure
   8.2 D – ignorant
   8.3 A – for

9. **9.1** B – 4
   9.2 D – 18
   9.3 A –500

10. **10.1** 5729
    10.2 6854
    10.3 6429

11. **11.1** 11 (multiply)
    11.2 840 (multiply, then times ten)
    11.3 82 (add)

12. **12.1** y (survey, yeast, vacancy, yield)
    12.2 p (plump, pledge, usurp, permit)